D0991206

© THE BAKER & TAYLOR CO.

GOLD

GOLD

BLAISE CENDRARS

Being The Marvellous History of
General John Augustus Sutter

Translated from the French by
NINA ROOTES

MICHAEL KESEND PUBLISHING, LTD.
New York

*All rights reserved. No portion of this book may be
reproduced in any form or by any means without the
prior written permission of the publisher.*

*Translated from the French
L'or, ou la marveilleuse histoire du General Johann August Sutter*

*First American publication 1984
© 1960 Editions Denoël
English translation © 1982 Nina Rootes*

*Library of Congress Cataloging in Publication Data
Cendrars, Blaise, 1887–1961
    Gold: the marvellous history of General John
Augustus Sutter.
    Translation of: L'or.
    1. Sutter, John Augustus, 1803–1880 — Fiction.
2. California — Gold discoveries — Fiction. I. Title.
PQ2605.E550713   1983   843'.912   83-16253
ISBN 0-935576-08-8*

Manufactured in the United States of America

To Madame WOEHRINGEN

Citizeness of Hamburg,
Patroness of expeditions,
explorer, scholar, lover
of adventures and adventurers

IN MEMORY

of some delightful evenings
before the war in her
FOLLY at Sceaux.

B. C.

SAN FRANCISCO

It is there that you will read the history of General Sutter, who conquered California for the United States.

And who, already a multi-millionaire, was ruined by the discovery of gold on his estates.

You have long hunted in the Sacramento Valley, over that same country where I worked to reclaim the land.

Blaise CENDRARS: *Le Panama ou les Aventures de mes sept Oncles*, 1914.

Another story is that of the 900 millions mentioned in 'LE PANAMA', as well as the history of General Sutter, which I shall write one day, or which I shall take up here, later on, if I have not already published it in the meantime.

Blaise CENDRARS: *Pro Domo*, 1918.

FIRST CHAPTER

1

The working day had just ended. The country folk were coming home from the fields, some with hoes over their shoulders, others carrying baskets. Leading the procession were the young girls in their white bodices and pleated aprons. They had their arms entwined about each other's waists and were singing: -

Wenn ich ein Vöglein wär
Und auch zwei Flüglein hätt
Flög ich zu dir . . .

On the doorsteps of their cottages, old men were smoking long porcelain pipes, while the old women knitted long white stockings. In front of the inn, the 'Wild Man', they were drinking the local white wine, pouring it from earthenware jugs decorated with a curious motif: a bishop's crozier surrounded by seven red dots. People were conversing in small groups, decorously, without shouting or unnecessary gestures. The topic of every conversation was the heat, exceptionally intense for so early in the year, and the drought that already threatened the young crops.

It was the 6th of May, 1834.

A gang of ragamuffins were standing around a little Savoyard who was turning the handle of his Sainte-Croix organ, while his marmot terrorized the smaller children, for it was excited and had just bitten one of them. A black dog was pissing against one of the four bollards at the corners of the multi-coloured drinking-fountain. The last rays of the sun lit up the ornate façades of the houses. Smoke from the chimneys rose straight up into the pure evening air. A cart could be heard creaking across the distant plain.

Suddenly, these peaceable country folk were thrown into consternation by the arrival of a stranger. Even in broad daylight, a stranger is something of a rarity in this little village of Rünenberg in the canton of Basle, but what were they to make of a stranger who turned up at such an unheard-of hour, so late in the evening, just as the sun was going down? The black dog froze with one leg in the air and the old women dropped their knitting. The stranger had just emerged from the road that led to Soleure. At first, the children moved towards him, but then they halted, hesitant and dubious. As for the group of drinkers at the 'Wild Man Inn', they had stopped drinking and were furtively eyeing the unknown man. The latter had called at the first house in the village and asked if someone would kindly point out the Mayor of the Commune's house. Old Buser, whom he had addressed, turned his back on him and, catching hold of his grandson Hans by the ear, told him to conduct the stranger to the Mayor. Then he went on filling his pipe, but all the while keeping a surreptitious eye on the stranger, who was striding away in the wake of the trotting child.

They saw the man enter the Mayor's house.

The villagers had had time, as he passed amongst them, to get a good look at the stranger. He was tall, lean, with a prematurely lined face. Odd tow-coloured hair stuck out beneath a hat with a silver buckle. He was wearing hob-nailed boots and carried a stout blackthorn

8

stick in one hand.

There was a burst of criticism. 'These strangers don't even have the courtesy to bid one good-day,' said Buhri, the innkeeper, clasping his hands across his enormous paunch. 'Listen, I bet you he's from the city,' said old Siebenhaar who, at one time, had done military service in France, and he started to tell them, yet again, about the curious things and the outrageous people he had come across amongst those 'bloody foreigners'.

The young girls had particularly noticed the straight cut of his frock-coat and the detachable collar with high points that chafed the lobes of his ears; they were gossiping in low voices, blushing and flustered. As for the boys, they had formed a menacing group about the fountain; they were awaiting developments, ready for action if need be.

Before long, the stranger reappeared on the threshold. He seemed very weary and was carrying his hat in his hand. He wiped his forehead with one of those large yellow silk scarves woven in Alsace. All at once, the little boy, who had been waiting for him on the steps, stood up, very erect. The stranger patted his cheek, then he gave him a *thaler* and strode across the village square, spitting into the fountain as he passed. Now every eye in the village was on him. The drinkers were on their feet. But the stranger never so much as spared them a glance; he climbed back into the cart which had brought him and disappeared rapidly down the road planted with service-trees that leads to the chief town of the canton.

This sudden apparition and precipitate departure caused havoc amongst the peaceful villagers. The little boy had started to cry. The silver coin the stranger had given him was passed round from hand to hand. Heated discussions broke out. The innkeeper was amongst the most vociferous. He was outraged that the stranger had not even deigned to stop for a moment at his inn to quaff a jug of wine. He suggested ringing the tocsin to warn the neighbouring villages and organizing a man-hunt.

Word soon went around that the stranger claimed to be a native of the commune and that he had come to ask for a Certificate of Origin, together with a passport, in order to undertake a long voyage abroad, but that he had not been able to prove his citizenship and the Mayor, who did not know him from Adam and had never set eyes on him before, had refused him both certificate and passport. Everyone agreed, volubly, that the Mayor had been most prudent.

This is the dialogue that took place the following morning in the office of the Secretary of Police in Liestal, the chief town of the canton. It was just on eleven o'clock.

The old Clerk of the Court: Will you issue a passport for France in the name of Johann August Suter, native of Rünenberg?

Kloss, the Secretary of Police: Has he got a Certificate of Origin issued by the Mayor of his Commune?

Old Clerk: No, he hasn't, but his father was a friend of mine and I'll stand guarantor for him.

Kloss, the Secretary of Police: Then I'm not issuing a passport. The boss is away. He can do what he likes about this sort of thing, but unfortunately he's at Aarau, and I'm not going to issue a passport under these circumstances.

Old Clerk: Listen, old man, aren't you pushing it a bit? I've told you, his father was a friend of mine, what more do you need?

Kloss, the Secretary of Police: My dear Gäbis, I'm only doing my duty. The rest does not concern me. I don't issue passports without a Certificate of Origin.

Late that evening, a warrant for his arrest arrived from Berne, but the stranger had already crossed the Swiss border.

2

Johann August Suter had just deserted his wife and four children.

He crossed the Swiss frontier below Mariastein; then, skirting the edge of the woods, he reached the mountains on the far side. The weather was still very hot and the sun scorching. That same evening, Suter reached Férette and, as a violent storm broke out, spent the night in a disused barn.

Next day, he set out again before dawn. He fell back towards the south, avoided Delle, crossed the Lomont and entered the district of the Doubs.

He had just walked more than twenty-five miles at a single stretch. Hunger gnawed at his stomach. He hadn't a farthing in his pocket. The *thaler* he had given to the urchin in Rünenberg had been his last coin.

He wandered on for two more days in the high, deserted pastures of the Franches-Montagnes, at nights prowling around the farms until the barking of the dogs

11

drove him back into the cover of the woods. One evening, however, he managed to milk a cow into his hat and greedily gulped down the warm, foaming milk. Up till then, he had had nothing but some tufts of wild sorrel and a few stalks of flowering gentian to suck on. He had found the first strawberry of the season and would carry the memory of it with him for many a long day.

Patches of snow were hardening in the shade of the fir-trees.

3

At this time, Johann August Suter was thirty-one years old.

He was born on the 15th of February, 1803, at Kandern in the Grand-Duchy of Baden.

His grandfather, Jakob Suter, founder of the dynasty of 'Suter, paper-manufacturers', as they are described in the register of the church at Kilchberg in Basle, had left the little commune of Rünenberg at the age of fifteen to take up his apprenticeship in the city. Some ten years later, he had become the largest manufacturer of paper in Basle and his dealings with the small university towns of Southern Germany had so greatly expanded that he set up new paper mills in Kandern. It was Hans Suter, father of Johann August, who managed this latter enterprise.

All this was in the good old days of the trade-guilds. The master paper-maker still signed contracts and commitments with his clerks and his workmen for a hundred and one years, and each spring his wife, the *patronne*, boiled the depurative herb tea that her own family and those of the workers all drank together. The secrets of paper-manufacturing were passed down from father to son and, as business expanded, new enterprises, all connected with the manufacture and commercial use of paper – printing, fancy papers, wallpapers, books, bookselling, publishing – became the patrimony of new members of the family. Each new generation, by specializing, gave new impetus to the ancestor's paper business, already well-known and soon to become famous throughout Europe.

(For example, Friedrich Suter, an uncle of Johann August's, dealt in illegal revolutionary pamphlets and broadsheets, smuggling enormous quantities of printed matter from Switzerland into Alsace and distributing it all over the country between Altkirch and Strasbourg. This earned him the right, under the title of 'famous propagandist', to witness the Terror in Paris in 1793 and 1794, and he has left a memoir full of details not published elsewhere. Even today, one of the last descendants of the great paper-master, Gottlieb Suter by name, is an established bookbinder in Basle, in that ancient and peaceful square where the little schoolgirls circle round the statue of the peasant-poet of the canton, holding hands and singing:

> *Johann Peter Hebel*
> *Hat zwischen den Bein' ein Knebel*
> *Und dass man ihn besser fassen kann*
> *Hat er zwei grosse Knollen drann*

It is just a tiny workshop. Gottlieb, a little mad, is a devotee of religious sects and denominations, and he preaches to the convicts in prison. He changes his religion more frequently than his shirt and beats his children black and blue. Very often, he will spend hours in a public house, soliloquizing over his glass and forgetting to go home. Since the time of the General, all the Suters have been that way inclined.)

4

Some two miles from Besançon, Johann August Suter is soaking his bruised and blistered feet in a stream. He is sitting amongst the buttercups, thirty yards from the highroad.

Ten or eleven German youths come out of a small, purplish wood and pass along the road. They are cheerful young fellows making a tour of France. One of them is a goldsmith, one works in wrought iron, a third is a butcher's boy and another a footman. Presently, they all gather round Johann and introduce themselves. They are a jolly bunch of rascals, always ready for a booze-up or a tumble in the hay. They are in shirt-sleeves and carry bundles tied to sticks. Johann joins their little band, passing himself off as a printer.

Suter arrives in Burgundy with these lads. One night, at Autun, while his companions are sleeping, overcome by wine, he ransacks the luggage of two or three of them and undresses one completely.

Next day, Suter is hot-foot on the road to Paris.

By the time he arrives there, he is once more penniless. He does not hesitate. He goes straight to a wholesale paper-merchant in the Marais district who is one of his father's best clients. He presents him with a forged letter-of-credit. Half an hour after pocketing the proceeds, he is in the courtyard of the *Messageries du Nord*, where he boards the stage-coach to Beauvais. From there he travels, via Amiens, to Abbeville. The skipper of a fishing-boat agrees to take him aboard and carry him to Le Havre. Three days later, the cannon booms, the bells ring out, the whole population of Le Havre is on the quays: the *Espérance*, a square-rigged paddle-steamer, sails proudly out of port and crosses the harbour boom. It is her maiden voyage. Destination: New York.

On board is Johann August Suter, bankrupt, fugitive, vagabond, thief and swindler.

He holds his head high and uncorks a bottle of wine.

And it is at this point that he disappears into the mists of the Channel; it is drizzling and the sea is choppy. In his own country, no more is heard of him and it is fourteen years before his wife has news of him. And then, suddenly, his name is uttered in tones of astonishment throughout the entire world.

Here begins the marvellous history of General John Augustus Sutter, as he is to be known in future.

It is a Sunday.

SECOND CHAPTER

The port.
The port of New York.
1834.

It is here that all the shipwrecked souls from the Old World disembark. The shipwrecked, the wretched, the discontented. Free men, men who refuse to submit. Those who have known the reverses of fortune, those who have risked all on the turn of a single card, those who have been ruined by a romantic passion. The first German socialists, the first Russian mystics. Ideologists wanted by the police in Europe; men hunted by the forces of reaction. Small tradesmen, the first victims of the early days of mass production. French phalansterians, Carbonari, the last disciples of Saint-Martin, the unknown philosopher, and Scotsmen. Generous souls and crackpots. Calabrian brigands, Hellenic patriots. Peasants from Ireland and Scandinavia. Individuals and nations, victims of the Napoleonic Wars, men sacrificed by Diplomatic Congresses. Carlists, Poles, Hungarian partisans. Visionaries from all the revolutions of 1830, and the last liberals, leaving their homelands to join the Great Republic; workers, soldiers, craftsmen, bankers of all nations, even South Americans, accomplices of Bolivar. Not since the French Revolution, not since the Declaration of Independence (and this is twenty-seven years before Lincoln's election to the Presidency) have the quays of New York seen such a continuous invasion:

the city is in the full flower of her growth and expansion. Day and night the emigrants disembark, and on every boat, amongst each human cargo, there is at least one representative of the hardy race of adventurers.

John Augustus Sutter disembarks on the 7th of July, a Tuesday. He has made a vow. At the quayside, he jumps down to the ground, elbows his way through the militiamen, takes in the vast maritime panorama at a single glance, uncorks a bottle of Rhine wine and empties it at one draught; he throws the empty bottle in amongst the Negro crew of a Bermudaman. Then he bursts out laughing and runs off into the great, unknown city, as if he were in a hurry and someone was expecting him.

6

'Listen, old man,' said Paul Haberposch to John Augustus Sutter, 'I'm offering you a nice cushy job, and you'll get your bed and board and laundry. I'll even kit you out with clothes. I've got an old highwayman's coat with seven capes – it'll knock the eyes out of those Irish immigrants! You won't find such a good position anywhere else, especially since, between you and me and the gate-post, you don't speak the language. But that highwayman's coat of mine will work wonders with the Irish. Believe me, they're a bunch of bloody fine rascals, every last man of 'em a son of the Devil dropped stark naked from heaven, and all you'll have to do is keep your ears open and you'll hear them going on in that God-forsaken, whore-stricken tongue of theirs, for they never know when to shut their gobs. I swear to you that, within a week, you'll hear such horrors that you'll be begging me to let you take Holy Orders. An Irishman can't keep his mouth shut, but what I want you to do, while he's getting it all off his chest, is to have a little feel of his bundle of luggage, see whether it's got a double stomach like a red monkey or if it's stuffed as tight as an old woman with constipation. I'll give you my coat, half a gallon of Bay Rum (you must always drink a toast with an Irishman who's fresh off the boat, it's the way to welcome him amongst his compatriots), and a little knife of my own invention. It's as long as your arm and as flexible as a eunuch's prick. You see this knob here? Press on it . . . there, d'you see? There are three little claws that come out of the end of the blade. Yes, that's the way. So, while you're rabbiting on to him about O'Connor or the Act of Union that's been voted through Parliament, my little tool will tell you whether your customer's arse is punched, bored or reamered. Then all you'll have to do is bite on it to discover whether his coin is made of gold or lead. Got it? Good, about bloody time, too! Sure, it's my own invention. When I was sailing around the ports of the Levant, we had a real bastard of a surgeon aboard, a Frenchman, and he used to call that thing a thermometer. Well, then, I entrust my thermometer to you, and no tricks, huh? I like the look of you, my boy, your mother didn't make a bad job of it when she had you. Listen. Whatever you do, don't forget to polish the buttons on that highwayman's coat, they must shine like the sign of a good pub, then you show them the flagon of rum, for, as the proverb says, "Good blood tells no lies," and with your hair like a bunch of radishes, my highwayman's coat, and the buttons polished till they glitter like dollars won at dice, they'll take you for the Bishop of Dublin's coachman on a day of General Indulgence, and, with their European notion of things, they'll follow you here like lambs, every one of 'em. But play it smart, eh? Don't get pipped at the post by that goddamned Dutchman over the road, or he'll snatch your clients from under your very nose . . . and, if he gets hold of them, watch out! One word more: once you've brought one of these wretched Irishmen here, make sure you never run into him again as long as you live, not even a hundred years from now! I wouldn't wish *that* on you. And now, bugger off, at the double!'

'Sometimes, you'll get a tip straight from the horse's mouth and sometimes you'll get a bum steer. But I'm going to teach you how to live off the fat of the land.'

It is Hagelstroem, the inventor of Swedish matches, speaking. John Augustus Sutter is his delivery boy, packer and bookkeeper. Three months have gone by. John Augustus Sutter has left the immediate neighbourhood of the port and penetrated further into the city. Like the entire American civilization, he is moving slowly westward. Since his encounter with that old pirate, Haberposch, he has already tried his hand at several trades. He is plunging more and more deeply into the life of the city. He works in a draper's shop, a drugstore, a delicatessen. He goes into partnership with a Rumanian and becomes a door-to-door salesman. He works as a groom in a circus. Then, as a shoeing-smith, a dentist, a taxidermist; he sells Jericho roses from a gilded wagon, sets up as a ladies' tailor, works in a sawmill, boxes a giant Negro and wins a slave and a purse of one hundred guineas; for a time, he is down-and-out; he teaches mathematics with the Mission Fathers, learns English, French, Hungarian, Portuguese,

19

the Negro dialect of Louisiana, Sioux, Comanche, American slang, Spanish. Advancing still further towards the West, he moves to the other side of the city, crosses the river, reaches the outskirts and opens a saloon in an outlying suburb. At Fordham, he has a clientele of tough wagon-drivers who like to linger over their drinks whilst exchanging all the news and gossip from the interior; among them, there appears from time to time a solitary and taciturn drinker. His name is Edgar Allan Poe.

Two years have elapsed. Everything that Sutter has heard, seen and learned, every conversation he has eavesdropped on, is engraved upon his memory. He knows New York, the little old streets with Dutch names and the great new arteries which are being laid out and numbered; he knows what kinds of business are carried on there, and which ones are creating the prodigious fortunes that are building up this city; he keeps himself informed of the progress of those slow caravans of wagons that cross the vast plains of the Middle West; he has his ear to the ground and learns of plans of conquest and exploration even before the government gets to hear of them. He has drunk so much whisky, brandy, gin, *eau-de-vie*, rum, *caninha, pulque* and *aguardiente*, with all the derelict souls who have returned from the interior, that he is now one of the best-informed men in the country about all that concerns the legendary territories of the West. His head is full of maps and itineraries, he has wind of several gold-mines, is the only one to know of certain hidden tracks. Two or three times he risks his money on distant expeditions or stakes it on the leader of this or that band. He knows Jews who will put up money, who are, so to speak, the organizers or patrons of enterprises of this sort. He also knows which officials can be bribed.

And he acts.

At first, cautiously.

He joins forces – for the journey only – with some German merchants who are leaving for St Louis, the capital of Missouri.

7

The State of Missouri is half as big as France. The sole route of communication is the gigantic Mississippi River. There it receives its principal tributaries: first, the formidable waters of the Missouri. Large steam ferries, fitted with a transverse wheel at the stern, sail 1,800 miles up this river, whose waters are so pure that, eighteen miles after their confluence, they can still be distinguished from the muddy, turbid, sickly-yellowish waters of the Mississippi; then there is a second river, probably as important and with waters just as pure, the 'beautiful river', the Ohio. Between the low-lying and densely-forested banks, these three rivers purl majestically to their meeting-place.

These giant arteries keep the ever-increasing and feverishly active populations of the eastern and southern states in touch with the unknown territories that stretch endlessly to the north and to the west. More than eight hundred steamboats a year berth in St Louis.

It is just above the capital, in the fertile angle formed by the confluence of the Missouri and the Mississippi (at St Charles to be precise), that John Augustus Sutter buys some land and settles down to farm.

It is a beautiful, fertile country. Maize, cotton and

tobacco grow there, but above all, further to the north, wheat. All this produce is sent down the river, to the warmer states, where it is rationed out daily to the Negroes who work on the sugar-cane plantations. It is a profitable trade.

But the thing that Sutter finds most interesting in all this busy traffic, is the lively discourse of the people who travel up and down the rivers. He keeps open house and there is always food on the table. An armed sloop, manned by black slaves, hails passing boats and leads them to the pier. So warm is the welcome that the house is always full; adventurers, settlers, trappers who are going down loaded with loot, or poor, penniless wretches, all are equally delighted to indulge themselves there and recover from the hardships of the bush and the prairie; going the other way, up-river, are fortune-hunters and daredevils, hotheads with fever in their eyes, mysterious, secretive men.

Sutter is indefatigable, he regales them all, drinks the night away, tirelessly interrogating his guests.

In his mind, he analyses, classifies and compares all these stories that he hears. He remembers every word and never forgets the name of a mountain, a pass or a river, or place-names such as Dry Tree, Three Horns, Bad Man's Ford.

One day, an illuminating idea strikes him. Every last one of the travellers who have filed through his house – the liars, the chatterboxes, the braggarts, the loud-mouths, and even the most taciturn – all, *all* have uttered one immense word that sheds its grandeur over their tales. Those who speak it too often as well as those who speak it too rarely, the boastful, the timid, the hunters, the outlaws, the traders, the settlers, the trappers, all, all, all, all speak of the West, speak of nothing, in fact, but the West.

The West.

Mysterious word.

What is the West?

This is the notion that he has of it:

From the valley of the Mississippi to beyond the gigantic mountain ranges, vast territories stretch far, far away to the West: marvellously fertile lands and arid steppes reaching to infinity. The prairie. The homeland of countless tribes of Redskins and the huge herds of buffalo that ebb and flow like the tides of the ocean.

But then, beyond that?

There are Indian legends that tell of an enchanted country where the towns are built of gold and the women have but a single breast. Even the trappers who come down from the North with their cargoes of furs have heard, in their remote latitudes, tales of this wondrous country of the West where, they say, the fruit is made of gold and silver.

The West? But what is it? What is to be found there? Why do so many men make their way there, never to return? They are killed by the Redskins. But those who get through? They die of thirst. But those who survive the deserts? They are halted by the mountains. But the man who crosses the pass? Where is he? What has he seen? Why is it that so many of the travellers who pass through my house strike out for the North but, the moment they are in the wilderness, turn sharply towards the West?

Most of them go to Santa Fe, that Mexican colony deep in the Rocky Mountains, but these are nothing but common traders attracted by easy profit, they give no thought to what lies beyond.

John Augustus Sutter is a man of action.

23

He sells his farm and turns all his possessions into cash. He buys three covered wagons and stocks them with provisions. Armed with a double-barrelled gun, he mounts his horse. He joins a company of thirty-five merchants who are going to Santa Fe, more than eight hundred miles away. But the business is ill-prepared, the organization haphazard and his companions a bunch of ne'er-do-wells who rapidly fall by the wayside. Sutter, like the rest, would have lost everything, for it is too late in the season for such a venture, but he manages to establish himself amongst the Indians of these territories and to live by bartering and trading.

And it is there, among the Indians, that he learns of the existence of another country, extending even further to the West, well beyond the Rocky Mountains, beyond the vast sandy deserts.

And, at last, he knows its name.

California.

But in order to reach this country, he must first return to Missouri.

He is obsessed.

THIRD CHAPTER

8

June 1838, Fort Independence on the border of the State of Missouri, on the banks of the river of the same name:

The caravans are making ready.

A wild confusion of animals and equipment. People are shouting at one another in every language under the sun. Germans, Frenchmen, Englishmen, Spaniards, Indians and Negroes jostle one another busily.

People are setting off on horseback, in carriages and in long processions of covered wagons pulled by twelve pairs of oxen. Some leave on their own, others in large companies. Some are returning to the United States, others leaving them to make for the south, in the direction of Santa Fe, or for the north, towards the high pass that leads over the mountains.

The real pioneers who, with no thought of returning, are forging ahead to search for more fertile land or a corner somewhere that will be their new homeland, are very few and far between. Most of these people are traders, hunters or trappers who are equipping themselves against the extreme cold of the Hudson Bay territory. If they reach the banks of the great frozen rivers, which have no name as yet but where beavers and other beasts with valuable furs abound, they will come back in three, or perhaps in seven years; the traders, however, will return next year to renew their stock-in-trade. Amongst the departures watched by all is that of a small, well-armed party composed of John Augustus Sutter, Captain Ermatinger, five missionaries and three women. The garrison of the fort fires a salvo in their honour as they set out on the track that will lead them to the Far West, to California.

9

During the three months he has just spent at Fort Independence, John Augustus Sutter has matured his plan.

He has made up his mind.

He will go to California.

He knows the route as far as Fort Vancouver, the last fort, and if certain information he has managed to glean proves reliable, he will be able to press on still further.

As yet, California has not attracted the attention of either Europe or the United States. Yet it is a country of incredible riches. The Republic of Mexico has already seized the treasures accumulated by the Missions over the centuries, but there are still vast prairie-lands and countless herds of cattle there, to be had for the taking.

Who dares all, wins all.

Sutter must seize his opportunity.

He is ready.

10

The track stretches for thousands of miles, flanked every hundred miles by a wooden fort surrounded by a stockade. The garrisons are fighting the Redskins with every weapon at their disposal, including cannon. It is a war of horrors and atrocities. No quarter is given. Woe betide the little band of men that falls into the hands of the savages or rides into an ambush set up by scalp-hunters.

Sutter is firmly resolved.

He rides at the head of his party, mounted on his mustang, 'Wild Bill', and whistling an air they play on the fife at the carnival in Basle. He is thinking of the small boy in Rünenberg to whom he gave his last *thaler*. For a moment, he reins in his horse. Heads or tails? And while the coin soars skyward like a lark, he murmurs: Tails, I win, heads, I lose. It is tails. He will succeed. And, without even having halted his companions, he rides on again, full of renewed strength. His first and last moment of doubt has passed. Now, he will go on to the bitter end.

His travelling companions are Captain Ermatinger, an officer who is going to relieve the commander of Fort Boise; the five missionaries – Englishmen sent out by the Bible Society in London to study the dialects of the Cree Indian tribes, whose lands lie to the north of the Oregon – and the three women, all whites, who belong to these seven men. All the others will leave him during the course of the journey and Sutter will go on alone; that is, unless he persuades the three women to remain with him.

The track follows the right bank of the Missouri, then turns off to the left and for more than four hundred miles follows the eastern bank of the Nebraska River; it crosses the Rockies close to Fremont Peak, which attains a height of over 13,000 feet, very nearly as high as Mont Blanc. Our travellers have been following this route for three weeks now. They have crossed the unchanging, endlessly flat wilderness, the oceans of grass where daily storms of unimaginable violence erupt on the stroke of noon to last no longer than a quarter of an hour; the sky becomes serene again, a harsh blue against the green fringes of the horizon. They camp beneath the crescent moon attended by a solitary, brilliant star; in vain to think of sleep, myriads of insects buzz all around them, thousands of toads and frogs salute the gradual blossoming of the stars. Coyotes yap. It is dawn, the magical hour of the birds. The two unvarying notes of the partridge. On again, and the track flies beneath the swift hooves of the horses. Rifles in hand, they look out for possible prey. Deer bound across their path. Behind them, at the end of the track, the sun, like a huge orange, soars rapidly towards its zenith.

At last, they reach Evans' Pass, the great fault of the South. They are on the summit of the great rampart that separates the United States from the territories of the West, on the frontier, 7,000 feet above sea level, 960 miles from Fort Independence.

And now, onward!

There is no longer a beaten track.

There are still 1,400 miles to go from here to the

mouth of the Oregon, on the Pacific.

Onward! They must find their own way, since there is no track to follow.

On the 1st of August, they arrive at Fort Hall. The commanding officer is anxious to detain them. The Redskins are on the warpath. But Sutter wants to push on. They have already been through the territories of so many warring tribes! They set out again on the 4th of August. An escort accompanies them for the first three days.

On the 16th of August, they reach Fort Boise, where the Hudson Bay Company has a large warehouse. Captain Ermatinger, having rejoined his post, leaves them there. Two of the women stay behind to work for the Company store. The remnant of the little band continues on its way through country infested with Kooyutt Indians. There has been a terrible famine, the Indians are harpooning salmon, even though it is the close season. They are savage and menacing. The rivers swarm with their canoes.

Sutter and his companions cross the region of giant pine-forests and, at the end of September, reach Fort Vancouver, which is a great centre for the fur trade. The missionaries have finally arrived. The last of the women has died of the hardships en route.

Now Sutter is alone.

12

A determined man is always welcome in this lost outpost at the extremity of the American continent and Sutter is not without charm. He receives a number of advantageous offers but refuses them all, a prey to his obsession.

He wants to go to California.

But today, so close to his goal, he once again finds himself faced with apparently insurmountable obstacles.

The advice of the men at the post is unanimous. The overland journey is impossible. The Apache Indians have donned their war-paint. Only recently, they have massacred a party of bear-hunters who had ventured into the high valleys of the Cascades. There is only one way to reach California, and that is by sea. But there are no boats, and navigation is always perilous in these ocean latitudes. It is true, however, that a sailing-ship could make the voyage in three weeks.

Sutter does not wait to hear any more. He goes down to the waterfront. A three-masted barque is anchored in the river. She is the *Columbia* on her way to the Sandwich Islands. 'All roads lead to Rome,' as old Haberposch would have said. Sutter comes to an arrangement with the skipper, negotiates his passage and, on the 8th of November, when the *Columbia* weighs anchor, he is in the process of fixing up his sleeping-quarters on deck.

FOURTH CHAPTER

13

Sutter is hammering in a nail on which to hang up his hammock made of bark. As he is standing on tiptoe and straining upward, his trousers are stretched tight and a button pops off his braces. It is a brass button. It rolls along the deck. At once, a hideous yellowish dog throws itself upon it and brings it back to him. This is Beppo, or Beppino, a kind of sheep-dog that used to belong to Maria, the woman who died of exhaustion under the sequoia trees of Snake River in Idaho. Maria was a Neapolitan. And, in all his four years in America, this is the only thing that Sutter has acquired: this circus dog *manqué*, that does tricks and smokes a pipe with the sailors.

The long crossing is uneventful.

The ship is under full sail on a south-south-westerly course.

On the 30th of November, at around five in the evening, the sunset is ominously grey, darkened still further by masses of black cloud, but next morning the weather is fine again and the storm-jib and the fore-topmast staysail are set.

In the early hours of December the 4th, the wind is raging, the seas high. By eight o'clock, the gale has become even fiercer. Mounting seas wash repeatedly over the badly-caulked deck. Water pours into the storeroom and swamps the ship's stores, crates of biscuits, sacks of potatoes, rice, sugar, buckwheat, dried cod and bacon, constituting three months' supplies. The eight-man crew remain at their posts all that day and throughout the following night. By daylight temporary repairs, which were carried out in darkness, are reinforced. There is considerable damage. The bitts, or vertical posts holding the bowsprit, have snapped off at deck-level. With the aid of a block and tackle, makeshift stays are rigged and the bowsprit braced as firmly as possible. At eleven o'clock at night, on the second day, the wind drops and veers abruptly to the north-east, soon bringing rain and heavy squalls in its wake. The sails are lowered and the tack changed. Squalls continue throughout the night.

On the 7th of January, nothing to report except the sighting of a sperm whale. Dolphins and bonitos leap all round the vessel. The waves are not excessively high but the sea is very rough, for the waves are coming from two different directions and constantly break over the bows. Everyone is drenched.

On the 11th of February, masses of sargasso, or gulf-weed, are noticed around the ship.

On the 27th, they are in a region of flat calm, but the *Columbia* is shipping water and all hands are at the pumps. Dozens of flying fish lie stranded on the deck. Pumping-out is hard work. Water is coming in at the bows, extinguishing the galley-stoves. A strong current is carrying the ship off course, towards the east.

On the 5th of March, they are again hove-to. Everyone is on deck. The sun is shining brightly. the leak has at last been stopped. The crew are happy, they are setting out tanks to collect the rain that is expected in the evening. There is no drinking water on board, no water to cook the food in.

A lascar is talking: 'I've never seen coloured folks

anywhere that dress in such elaborate style as they do in Paraguay. The Negresses and the mulattoes construct great scaffolds on their heads, planting high tortoiseshell combs and flowers and feathers in their frizzy hair. They always wear gaudy colours and their dresses have long trains and low-cut necklines. In that country, it's always carnival time. The . . .'

Sutter is in his hammock. His dog is smoking. Now that the tanks are ready, the sailors are playing backgammon. A ship's boy, who has become Sutter's devoted admirer, is rocking the hammock.

At midnight, the beneficent rain falls and the ship again makes headway in a gentle breeze. A little later, she sails in amongst the islands. As the moon is full, Sutter, from his swinging hammock, can contemplate the foliage of the palm trees and the latanias in flower.

Sutter is enchanted by the voyage.

Grandiose plans form in his mind. He has not wasted his time and has acquired a whole mine of information that will be of use to him. He has made the skipper and the crew talk. Now he has gained an insight into the morals and manners of California, the resources and the needs of this mysterious country, for these rough sailors have already loaded dozens of cargoes there, cargoes of planks, hides and talc. To their way of thinking, the two shores of the Pacific form but a single unit, for they do just as good a trade with the American Indians as they do with the natives of the islands; they have had as frequent dealings with the Spanish missionaries of Monterey as with the American missionaries of Honolulu. Sutter begins to get some conception of the prodigious future that awaits this vast and still unexploited part of the globe. As his plans and ideas enlarge in scope and grandeur, so they become more precisely detailed. They go far beyond anything he could have imagined, and yet they are possible. Realizable. A splendid place is there for the taking. A *coup d'état*. He has both the taste for such an enterprise and the strength to risk it.

Meanwhile, he disembarks empty-handed in the capital, Honolulu, and presents his letters of recommendation (given to him by officials of the Hudson Bay Company in Fort Vancouver) to the trading post there.

Here, too, he finds a warm welcome.

14

Honolulu is a bustling capital.

The bulk of the population is made up, essentially, of maritime adventurers, mostly deserters from the whaling fleets. Naturally, every race in the world is represented there, but Basque and Yankee elements predominate. Sutter is enthusiastically adopted by every social class and he has the good fortune to run into some old acquaintances from New York. Together with them, he joins in several speculative ventures, buying up cargoes of copra, mother-of-pearl and tortoiseshell that are lying out in the roadsteads, and he is lucky enough to amass a small fortune very quickly.

During this period, the idea comes to him that he will employ a labour force of Kanakas, the Melanesians of New Caledonia, on his plantations of the future. It will take a lot of muscle-power to exploit California and reclaim the immense territories of the American West. Africa is too far away, and the Atlantic slave-trade is hampered by too much legislation these days. It is no longer possible to make a profit. Besides, it would be amusing to cock a snook at international regulations and avoid the reciprocal boarding rights between ships by starting the slave-trade in unsuspected latitudes. Cargoes of islanders could be forcibly embarked. The Pacific must learn to be self-sufficient.

He has already given his partners just a hint of his grandiose Californian schemes; now he broaches this new idea with them. That same evening, in a tavern, they sign the articles of constitution of Sutter's Pacific Trading Company, whose emblem is a black bishop's crozier surrounded by seven red dots on a white background. For his part, Sutter puts up 75,000 Dutch florins. The first consignment of Kanakas must arrive in eighteen months' time at the latest; they will disembark in a certain Californian bay whose whereabouts Sutter reveals in confidence. In the legal documents, his future possessions appear under the name of New Helvetia.

Once the covenants are signed, they indulge in an orgy of rum.

Now that this business is settled, he must think about departure, but that is no simple matter.

Sutter is in a hurry.

15

In the roadsteads, there was not a single vessel destined for the ports of Mexico, nor one that was willing to take him to San Diego. There was only a Russian ship, ready to sail for Sitka, a Russian trading centre far up the American coast, at the northern extremity of the Pacific.

The Russians, fanning out from Kamtchatka, were setting up numerous trading posts along the American coast. With the constant expansion of their empire, they were coming into collision with the growing power of the United States to the east; to the south, they had already reached the Mexican coast, where they had a number of colonies. Russian schooners plied regularly between Sitka and Mexico.

Sutter does not hesitate, he embarks at once and sails as far north as the Aleutian Islands. Moreover, he gets on very well with the Russians; he establishes a rapport with them and assures himself of their support. But he has no intention of spending the rest of his life in Sitka. He leaves at the first opportunity.

Aboard a swift schooner, he travels south, hugging the coast of Alaska, crossing the whaling-grounds, passing the mouth of the Oregon – well out to sea this time – moving further and further down the coast till, at last, he lands on the beach of San Francisco.

Sutter is alone on the shore. The high billows of the Pacific roll up to his feet and expire. The sailing-ship that landed him here is already out of sight, heading for Monterey. Foaming waves succeed one another, slowly, in parallel lines. At some distance from the water's edge, the sand takes on a greyish hue; ceaselessly battered by the waves, it is perfectly smooth and of a very solid consistency, offering the traveller a most convenient roadway that owes nothing to the efforts of man, and which stretches as far as the eye can see. A plant with long sprawling stems is the only thing that grows here and even that is sparse. Countless seagulls are lined up at the edge of the ocean, waiting for the waves to bring them their food. Other birds, whose name he does not know, are running along the beach at lightning speed, their heads outstretched in a line with their backs. Sea-swallows land and immediately take flight again. Some black birds are strolling up and down, always in pairs. There is also a large bird with feathers of a dark grey mingled with a paler shade; its beak is like an eagle's and it has a long horizontal plume at the back of its head.

When Sutter starts walking, he crushes a great many rose-coloured vesicular molluscs, which burst with a loud plop.

FIFTH CHAPTER

16

Ever since its discovery, California had always been linked with the crown of Spain. It formed one of the provinces of the Spanish Viceregency of Mexico. Neither its extent nor its configuration were known with any degree of exactitude. In 1828, when it finally became necessary to mark a northern boundary to this immense country, a straight line, at right angles to the ocean, was drawn on an atlas: it started at Cape Mendocino and finished at Evans' Pass, the great southern fault of the Rocky Mountains – a straight line more than fourteen hundred miles long.

Baja California is a peninsula, almost an island, that juts out into the Vermilion Sea; although well-known, it is an unproductive, scarcely-inhabited region; as for Upper California, further north, it has hardly been explored. It is known that a mountainous chain runs the whole length of the coast and that, behind it, there is a second range, a little higher, which likewise runs from north to south; also, that there is yet a third range behind it, lying parallel to the two preceding chains. This is the Sierra Nevada, with its formidable peaks. The valleys between these three mountain ranges consist, in part, of vast plains. Behind the sierra stretches the great Californian desert, as far as the edges of the Great Basin, and beyond the great Salt Lake, the prairie and the steppes begin again.

In 1839, this bipartite territory forms a province of

38

the Republic of Mexico. It is administered by the Governor, Alvarado. The seat of government is Monterey, on the mainland. It has a population of about 35,000 inhabitants, of whom 5,000 are whites and the rest Indians.

17

Imagine a strip of land running from London to the oases of the Sahara and from St Petersburg to Constantinople. This strip of land is entirely coastal. Its land-mass is considerably larger than that of France. The North is exposed to the most rigorous winters, the South is tropical. A long, deep canyon, which cuts through two chains of mountains and divides this strip of land into two exactly equal parts, connects a great inland lake with the sea. This lake could accommodate all the fleets in the world. Two majestic rivers, which have irrigated the regions of the interior to the north and to the south, come to pour their waters into it. These are the Sacramento and the Joaquin. This is all we need remember about this vast province of California, and it is this crude sketch of it that Sutter consults in his notebook.

He has just paddled up the channel and crossed the lake in a little pirogue with a triangular sail.

He sets foot on land in front of the poverty-stricken Mission Post. A Franciscan, consumed with fever, comes to meet him.

He is in San Francisco.

Fishermen's huts made of beaten earth. Blue-skinned pigs wallowing in the sun, lean sows with dozens of piglets.

This is what John Augustus Sutter has come to conquer.

18

The moment is particularly well-chosen.

Although it is far from the political centre of the world, and outside the mainstream of contemporary history at the beginning of the nineteenth century, California has just come through a series of acute crises. Events that may be no more than a nine days' wonder in the metropolis can often have the most terrible and far-reaching consequences in countries at the far ends of the earth; the repercussions may transform the old way of life from top to bottom or shatter the new and still fragile civic order.

California's position was extremely precarious. Its very existence was in jeopardy.

The Mission settlements, which the Jesuits had built throughout the territory of Old California as in all the other countries overseas, had passed into the hands of the Franciscans when the Jesuits were expelled in 1767. The Franciscans had undertaken the colonization of New California, where the Jesuits had never penetrated.

Little by little, making their way slowly up the coast, the Fathers had established themselves in eighteen posts which were no more than simple settlements at first, but which, in the course of a few years, had become important estates surrounded by prosperous villages.

Everywhere, the organization was the same and followed a single pattern.

40

The most important of these colonies, San Luis Rey, was composed of a group of buildings arranged in a square. Each façade was 450 feet in length. The church occupied one whole side by itself. The other three were taken up by the living quarters, the farm with all its outbuildings, stables, cattle-byres, barns, storehouses and workshops. Within the square was a courtyard planted with sycamores and fruit trees. In the centre of the courtyard, a great jet of water rose from a monumental fountain. The infirmary was tucked away in one of the most secluded corners.

Two Capuchin friars were responsible for the domestic chores, the others busied themselves in the school, the workshops and warehouses, or took care of travellers.

The young Indian girls were under the supervision of Indian matrons; they were taught to weave woollen, linen or cotton fabrics; they did not leave the Mission until it was time for them to marry. The most gifted young people learned music and singing, the others, some manual skill or agriculture.

The Indians were divided into brigades, each under the leadership of one of their chiefs. At 4 a.m. every day, the Angelus was rung and everyone attended Mass. After a frugal breakfast, the workers went out to the fields. From 11 a.m. to 2 p.m., they had a meal in the open air followed by a rest. At sundown, there was another religious service which all, including the sick, were obliged to attend; then there was supper, and afterwards, singing and dancing which often went on far into the night. The food consisted of beef or mutton, cereals and green vegetables; there was nothing but water to drink. The men wore a long linen shirt, cotton trousers and a long woollen cloak; the women were given two blouses a year each, plus a skirt and a coat.

The *alcalde* and the other native chiefs were dressed like the Spanish.

After their products – hides, talc and cereals – had been sold and loaded on to foreign ships, the Fathers distributed books, lengths of cloth, tobacco, rosaries and cheap knick-knacks to the Indians. Another portion of the revenue was devoted to the embellishment of the church, the purchase of paintings, statues and valuable musical instruments. One quarter of the harvest was kept in storage.

Each year, more and more land was brought under cultivation. The Indians built bridges, roads, canals and windmills under the direction of the monks, or worked in the various workshops: horse-shoeing, harness-making, lock-making, dyeing and cleaning clothes, tailoring, saddlery, carpentry, pottery and tile-making.

Very gradually, other small dominions were created all around the mother-house: land was cleared, farms and small plantations entrusted to the care of a particularly worthy Indian. In 1824, the Mission of San Antonio, for example, was able to count 1,400 Indians who possessed between them 12,000 head of cattle, 2,000 horses and 14,000 sheep. The Fathers themselves had taken a vow of poverty and possessed nothing in their own right, considering themselves trustees and stewards of the Indians.

Then came the Republic of Mexico. In 1832, the religious foundations and their settlements were declared State property. The friars were promised a pension, but it was never paid. And what booty there was to be had! Generals and political opportunists appropriated the richest domains, and the Indians – maltreated, wretched, stripped of everything – retreated into the wilderness and the bush. Public prosperity and well-being soon foundered. By 1838, there were already only 4,450 paid workers left out of the 30,650 Indians who had worked as free men in the Missions; the herds of cattle fell from 420,000 horned beasts to 28,220; the horses from 62,500 to 3,800; the sheep from 321,500 to 31,600. Then the government made one last effort to restore the old wealth and prosperity. They gave land to the Indians, declared them to be citizens of a free Republic, with full civil rights. But it was too late. The damage was done. The Mission settlements had been transformed into brandy distilleries.

It is at this moment that Sutter disembarks.

And he soon makes his presence felt.

SIXTH CHAPTER

19

His first expedition on horseback has brought Sutter into the Sacramento Valley. The incredible fertility of the soil and the luxuriant vegetation decide for him: he will settle here. Returning from this reconnaissance, he learns that the first convoy of Kanakas has just landed. There are 150 of them and they are housed in the hamlet of Yerba Buena, at the far end of the Bay of San Francisco. His partners in Honolulu have engaged nineteen whites to come over with them; they are tough, cheerful men, hard-bitten and ready for anything. Sutter reviews them. They are armed to the teeth.

Immediately, Sutter makes the overland journey to Monterey. He does it at a single stretch, riding night and day.

John Augustus Sutter presents himself to Governor Alvarado. He announces his intention of setting up in the country. His Kanakas will clear the land. His small armed band will form a vigilant cordon to prevent incursions by the totally hostile tribes to the north. He intends to reassemble the Indians from the former Missions, distribute land to them and set them to work under his direction.

'More and more ships,' he says, 'will be coming from Honolulu, where I have formed a substantial company. New convoys of Kanakas will be landing in the bay which I have chosen and further teams of white men will arrive with them, men in my pay. Give me a free hand,

and I will get the country back on its feet.'

'And what do you propose to call your ranch?'

'*New Helvetia.*'

'Why?'

'Because I am Swiss and a Republican.'

'Good. Do what you want. I will grant you a concession for ten years, in the first instance.'

20

Sutter and his troop travel up the Sacramento Valley.

At the head sail three ex-whalers, still decked out for sea and with a small cannon aboard. Then come the 150 Kanakas dressed in horizontally-striped shirts that reach down to their knees. They have made themselves odd little pointed hats from the leaves of tulip-trees. Following them along the banks and through the swamps are thirty wagons loaded with provisions, seeds and munitions, as well as some fifty horses, seventy-five mules, five bulls, two hundred cows and five flocks of sheep. The rearguard, some on horseback, some in canoes, with rifles slung across their backs and leather caps tilted over one ear, are keeping close ranks and driving everyone forward when the going gets rough.

21

Six weeks later, the valley presents a ghostly spectacle. Fire has swept this way, a fire that smouldered under the low-hanging, acrid smoke of the bracken and the shrubby trees before flaring up like a torch, high, straight, implacable, in a single blaze. On all sides now, they see smoking stumps, twisted bark, splintered branches. The great solitary trees are still standing, but riven, scorched by the flames.

There is work to be done!

The oxen plod to and fro. The mules pull the plough. Seed is scattered. There is not even time to root out the blackened stumps, so the furrows skirt round them. The cattle are already wallowing in the marshy prairies, the sheep are on the hills and the horses are grazing in a paddock surrounded by thorn-bushes. At the confluence of two rivers, they are throwing up earthworks and building the ranch-house. Roughly-hewn tree-trunks and planks six inches thick are used in its construction. Everything is solid, large, massive, conceived for the future. The buildings are laid out in a line: barns, storehouses and granaries. The workshops are on the banks of the river, the Kanaka village in a ravine.

Sutter keeps an eye on everything, directs everything, supervises the execution of the work down to the last detail; he is at every work-site at once and does not hesitate to put his hand to the task personally when one or other of the work-gangs is a man short. Bridges are built, tracks cleared, swamps drained, a well sunk, ponds, drinking-troughs and irrigation channels dug. A first palisade already protects the farm, a small fort is planned. Emissaries scour the Indian villages, and 250 of the Indians formerly protected by the Missions are brought in, together with their wives and children, to work on the various projects. Every three months, new convoys of Kanakas arrive and the lands under cultivation now stretch as far as the eye can see. Thirty-odd whites, men who have been settlers in this country for

46

some time, come to offer their services. They are Mormons. Sutter pays them three dollars a day.

And prosperity is not long in coming.

4,000 oxen, 1,200 cows, 1,500 horses and mules and 12,000 sheep are dispersed around New Helvetia, covering an area that takes several days to walk round. The harvests yield 530 per cent and the granaries are full to bursting.

As early as the end of the second year, Sutter is able to buy some fine farms along the coast, near Fort Bodega. They belong to the Russians, who are pulling out. He pays 40,000 dollars cash for them. He plans to go in for stock-breeding on the grand scale there and, more particularly, to improve the bovine strain.

22

In colonizations of this kind, it is sometimes possible to overcome the difficulties of a purely material nature, that arise day by day, with relative ease; a will of iron and strenuous labour, backed up by suitable equipment, may succeed in imposing a new order on the secular laws of nature, and even in transforming the aspect of a virgin land and the climatology of a region forever, but the human element is not so easily mastered.

From this point of view, John Augustus Sutter's position was absolutely typical.

At the moment of his arrival, California was on the brink of a revolution. In Mexico itself, the Compañia Cosmopolitana had just been formed with the avowed aim of pillaging what was left of that unhappy country once occupied by the Mission settlements. Powerful political groups had just embarked a force of two hundred adventurers to be unleashed on this so-recently-prosperous land. While these men were at sea, General Santa Anna overthrew President Farias and immediately sent a courier, via Sonora, to Governor Alvarado giving him strict orders to oppose the landing of these roughnecks by force. The band was broken up just off San Diego, between the Pacific and the bay, and those of its members who managed to escape infested the country, giving themselves up to banditry. Two gangs were formed and the partisans put the country to fire and blood. Sutter was wise enough not to interfere, and skilful enough to come to terms with both factions. However, hunters, trappers and fur-traders, all of American nationality, had infiltrated into the very heart of the region, and they formed a small but very active nucleus who wanted California to join the Union. Here again, Sutter was able to manoeuvre without compromising himself, for, while the Americans benefited from his secret support (every six months he sent a courier over the mountains to carry his reports to St Louis; one of his messengers even presented himself in Washington, to submit a plan of conquest: Sutter demanded personal command of the troops and exacted one-half of the territories conquered as his reward), in the eyes of the Mexicans, his heroic conduct on the frontier, where he energetically repelled the constant incursions of savage tribes, made him appear as such a faithful ally of the government that they gave him the title Guardian of the Northern Frontier, with the rank of captain. And, to recompense him for his services, Alvarado made him a grant of eleven square leagues of land, an area as vast as the little canton of Basle, his homeland.

The Indians were Sutter's biggest headache.

The savage tribes of the Upper Sacramento looked askance upon his settlement. These ploughed lands, these farms with their flocks and herds, these buildings that sprang up everywhere, were encroaching on their hunting grounds. They had taken up arms and, by night, set fire to barns and haystacks while, in broad daylight, they murdered the lonely shepherds and raided the cattle. There were frequent armed clashes, shots were exchanged and never a day passed but a dead man was carried back to the farmhouse: the scalped corpse of a woodcutter, a hideously-mutilated planter or a militiaman struck down from behind. Never had Sutter had such good reason to congratulate himself on his brainwave of importing a Kanaka work-force as during these first two years of incessant skirmishes. Without them, he could never have achieved his goal.

There were six villages full of these islanders.

23

In spite of the struggles, the battles, the political complications, the ever-present threat of revolution, in spite of murders and fire-raising, John Augustus Sutter was proceeding methodically with his plan.

New Helvetia was taking shape.

The dwelling-houses, the ranch-house, the principal buildings, the granaries and warehouses were now surrounded by a wall five feet thick and twelve feet high. At each corner stood a rectangular bastion, armed with three cannon. Six other guns defended the main entrance. There was a permanent garrison of one hundred men. Further, all the year round, the immense domain was guarded by watchmen and patrols. The militiamen, recruited in the bars of Honolulu, had married Californian wives who accompanied them wherever they were posted, carrying the baggage, grinding corn and making bullets and cartridges. In times of danger, all these people fell back upon the small fort and helped to reinforce the garrison there. Two small boats, armed with cannon, were anchored in front of the fort, ready to sail up either the American River or the Sacramento.

The men who ran the sawmills (where the giant trees of the locality were sawn up) and the innumerable workshops were mostly ships' carpenters, helmsmen or boatswains who, while in port on the coast, had been persuaded to desert their sailing-ships for a wage of five dollars a day.

It was not unusual to see white men coming to the ranch-house to apply for work, attracted by the renown and the prosperity of the settlement. They were poor colonists who had not been successful on their own, mostly Russians, Irishmen and Germans. Sutter parcelled out land to them, or employed them according to their various skills.

Horses, hides, talc, wheat, flour, maize, dried meat, cheese, butter, planks and smoked salmon were embarked daily. Sutter sent his produce to Vancouver, Sitka, the Sandwich Islands and to all the ports of Mexico and South America, but, first and foremost, he provisioned the numerous ships that now came to drop anchor in the bay.

It was in this state of bustling prosperity that Captain Frémont found New Helvetia when he came down from the mountains after his memorable crossing of the

Sierra Nevada.

Sutter had gone out to meet him with an escort of twenty-five splendidly-accoutred men. The horses were stallions. The riders' uniforms were made of a dark green cloth relieved by yellow braid. With their caps tipped over one ear, the lads had a martial look about them. They were all young, strong and well-disciplined.

Countless flocks of prime beasts were grazing in the lush prairies. The orchards were glutted with fruit. In the kitchen-gardens, vegetables from the Old World grew side by side with those from tropical countries. There were springs and canals everywhere. The Kanaka villages were neat and clean. Every man was at his appointed task. A most pleasing order reigned everywhere. Avenues of magnolia, palm-trees, bananas, camphor-trees, oranges, lemons and pepper-plants traversed the vast cultivated tracts to converge on the ranch-house. The walls of the *hacienda* were smothered in bougainvillaea, rambler roses and fleshy geraniums. A curtain of jasmine hung down before the master's door.

Sutter kept a splendid table. Hors-d'oeuvres; trout and salmon from the local rivers; baked ham *à l'Ecossaise*; wood-pigeon, haunch of venison, bear's paw; smoked tongue; sucking-pig stuffed *à la rissole* and dredged with tapioca flour; green vegetables, cabbage-palm, okra salad; fruit of every kind, fresh and preserved; mountains of *pâtisserie*. Rhine wines and several bottles of fine old wines from France, which had been so carefully handled that they had travelled round the world without being spoiled. The food was served by young women from the Islands and young Indian half-breed women who brought in the dishes wrapped in napkins of a pristine whiteness. They came and went with an imperturbably serious air, while a Hawaiian orchestra

51

played outlandish airs, the *Marche de Berne*, with thumb-beats on the backs of the guitars, the *Marseillaise* with the sonorities of the bugle in the strings. The heavy antique tableware was made of Castilian silver-plate and struck with the royal arms.

Sutter presided, surrounded by his associates. Amongst the guests was Governor Alvarado.

24

Sutter was accredited with the most important banking-houses in both the United States and Great Britain. He made substantial purchases of materials, tools, arms and ammunition, seeds and plants. His transports travelled thousands and thousands of miles overland or came by sea after rounding Cape Horn. (Twenty-five years later, in the ranches in the hinterland, they still talked about a wagon pulled by sixty pairs of white oxen which, under heavy escort, crossed the entire American continent at its widest point; after crossing the prairies, the savannahs, the rivers, the fords, the mountain passes of the Rockies and the desert with its giant cactus-candelabra, it finally arrived safe and sound with its cargo, which consisted of the boiler and plant for the first steam-mill to be constructed in the United States. As will be seen later, it would have been better for John Augustus Sutter, then at the pinnacle of his success, wealth and prestige, if this wagon had never arrived, if it had foundered at the bottom of some river, if it had bogged down forever in some quagmire, if it had tumbled over some precipice or if its numerous teams of oxen had succumbed to an epidemic.)

However, political events were hastening forward.

And although Sutter was now a man to be reckoned with, to be listened to with respect, he was by no means sheltered from contingencies. Quite the contrary. Revolutions occurred one after the other. The struggle between opposing factions was fiercer than ever. Everyone wanted Sutter on their side, as much for his moral ascendancy as for his social position. Ultimately, each camp was counting on the contribution of the little army of New Helvetia. But Sutter never allowed himself to be drawn into these civil wars, and although, more than once, he saw his estates on the point of being invaded, his crops burned, his flocks scattered, his stores and granaries looted by yelling hordes who had just laid waste everything for hundreds of miles around, and who were excited by the sight of so much well-ordered wealth, he also knew how to extricate himself from these predicaments thanks to his profound knowledge of the human heart, acquired during his years of poverty in New York, and it was this which, in moments of crisis, sharpened his wits, his insight and his powers of argument. At such times, he was of a rare perspicacity, never put a foot wrong, schemed and manoeuvred, promised everything that was asked of him, audaciously bribed the leaders at precisely the right moment, sweetened men with brilliant arguments and with alcohol. As a last resort, he was prepared to have recourse to arms, but it was not so much a military victory that he desired (although force was on his side), as the safeguarding of his work, his labours, for he had no wish to see everything that he had just built up destroyed. And, in spite of everything, he was often on the brink of losing it all in a single day.

He kept in constant touch with the United States, and it was precisely from that direction, from the government in Washington, that he had most to fear.

As early as 1841, Captain Graham, at the head of forty-six English and American adventurers, had hoped, by a bold stroke, to seize power and proclaim the independence of California. But Alvarado had got wind of the affair; he surprised the conspirators, massacred more than half of them and threw the rest into prison. Immediately, London and Washington seized on the incident to claim compensation for the murder of their subjects. London demanded 20,000 dollars and the United States 129,200 dollars for fifteen riflemen. A British corvette lay in wait off Vera Cruz. The Mexicans were forced to submit.

In the spring of 1842, the revolt led by the Dominican monk, Gabriel, was put down in a blood-bath.

In October 1843, a band of more than a hundred Americans arrived from Santa Fe and Governor Alvarado, unpopular because of his despotic rule and in fear of new disturbances, asked Mexico for aid. Santa Anna, the President and dictator, sent three hundred galley-slaves by sea. He had promised them land, tools, cattle and the restoration of their civil rights if they could succeed in kicking out the Americans. At the same time, he appointed a new Governor of California, General Manuel Micheltorena. This general was an honest man, full of good intentions, but he could do nothing to uphold the Mexican domination, which was rapidly disintegrating. He chose to set up his quarters in the old Mission buildings of Santa Clara, Los Angeles. He frequently visited New Helvetia to take counsel, but

Sutter, for his part, was preoccupied with the unyielding attacks of the savages, which were causing terrible slaughter.

Five more years pass, years of struggles, uprisings, riots and revolutions fomented primarily by the Cabinet in Washington, then comes the war with Mexico and the cession of Texas and California to the United States.

Sutter has obtained a further grant of twenty-two square leagues of land from the last Mexican Governor.

He owns the largest domain in the States.

26

Peace at last.

A new era commences.

John Augustus Sutter will at last be able to enjoy, and rejoice in, his wealth and good fortune.

New seeds arrive from Europe and saplings of every kind of fruit-tree. He acclimatizes olive and fig-trees on the lower, more sheltered ground; apple and pear-trees on the hills. He starts the first cotton plantations and, on the banks of the Sacramento, experiments with rice and indigo.

And finally he realizes a desire that has long lain close to his heart: he plants vines. At great expense, he has vine-stock brought over from the Rhine and from Burgundy. In the northern part of his estates, on the banks of the Feather River, he has had built a sort of country seat or manor house. It is his retreat. The Hermitage. Clumps of tall trees shade the house. All around, there are gardens with huge beds of carnation and heliotrope. There his finest fruits grow, cherries, apricots, peaches and quinces. His choicest pedigree cattle graze in the meadows.

Now, every step leads him towards his vineyards. When he goes for a walk, it is to see his vines, his Hochheimer, his Chambertin, his Château-Chinon.

As he caresses his favourite dog in the shade of a pergola, he dreams of bringing his family over from Europe, of lavishly repaying his creditors, of regaining his civic rights and redeeming the honour of his name; also, of endowing his little birthplace, so far away . . . Sweet dreams.

My three sons will come, they will have work, they must be men by now. And my daughter, how is she? I know! I'll order a grand piano for her, from Pleyel in Paris. It will be brought along the route I travelled long ago, on the backs of bearers if need be . . . Maria . . . All my old friends . . .

Reverie.

His pipe has gone out. He gazes into the far distance. The first stars are coming out. His dog lies motionless.

Reverie. Calm. Repose.

It is Peace.

27

Reverie. Calm. Repose.

It is Peace.

No. No. No. No. No. No. No. No. No: it is GOLD!

It is gold.

The gold rush.

The world is infected with gold fever.

The great gold rush of 1848, 1849, 1850 and 1851. It will last for fifteen years.

SAN FRANCISCO!

EIGHTH CHAPTER

28

And all this is triggered off by the simple blow of a pickaxe.

These stampeding mobs of people. First, they come from New York and all the ports on the Atlantic coast, and then, immediately afterwards, from the hinterland and the Middle West. It is a veritable flood. Men pack themselves into the holds of steamers going to Chagres. Then they cross the isthmus, on foot, wading through the swamps. Ninety per cent of them die of yellow fever. The survivors who reach the Pacific coast charter sailing-ships.

San Francisco! San Francisco!

The Golden Gate.

Goat Island.

The wooden wharves, the muddy streets of the nascent town, which are paved with sacks full of flour.

Sugar costs five dollars, coffee ten, an egg twenty, an onion two hundred, a glass of water a thousand. Shots ring out and the 45 revolver does duty for a sheriff. And behind this first human wave come more, and still more, hurling themselves in a great tide, and coming now from much further away – from the shores of Europe, Asia, Africa, from North and South.

In 1856, more than six hundred ships enter the Bay; they disgorge an endless stream of people who instantly throw themselves into the search for gold.

San Francisco! San Francisco!

And another magic name: SUTTER.

The name of the workman who struck that famous blow with the pickaxe is not widely known.

It was James W. Marshall, a carpenter by trade and a native of New Jersey.

29

John Augustus Sutter, not merely the first American millionaire, but the first multimillionaire in the United States, is ruined by that blow of the pickaxe.

He is forty-five years old.

And after having ventured all, risked all, dared all and created for himself a way of life, he is ruined by the discovery of gold-mines on his lands.

The richest mines in the world.

The fattest nuggets.

The end of the rainbow.

30

But let us hear from John Augustus Sutter himself.

The following chapter is copied from a thick book whose parchment covers bear traces of fire. The ink has faded, the paper has yellowed, the spelling is shaky, the handwriting full of flourishes and curlicues; it is difficult to decipher, the language is full of idioms, phrases of Basle dialect and Amerenglish. While the hand that wrote it is touchingly awkward and full of hesitations, the narrative itself is told directly, simply, even stupidly. The writer has not one word of complaint, he confines himself to narrating the events, enumerating the facts just as they happened. He does not exaggerate in the slightest degree.

I humbly translate:

31

'Towards the middle of January 1848, Mr Marshall, the carpenter from New Jersey who is building my mills, was working on the new sawmill at Coloma, high up in the mountains, fifty miles distant from the fort. Once the framework had been erected, I sent Mr Wimmer and his family up there, together with a number of workmen; Mr Bennett, from Oregon, accompanied them to oversee the installation and setting-up of the machinery. Mrs Wimmer did the cooking for the whole party. I still required a sawmill as I was short of planks for my large steam-mill, which was also under construction, at Brighton. The boiler and machinery for this had just arrived after a journey of eighteen months. God be praised, I had never expected to see a successful outcome to this enterprise, and all the oxen survived, thank the Lord. I also needed planks for the construction of other buildings and especially for a stockade around the village of Yerba Buena, at the far end of the bay, for there are now many vessels in the harbour and the crews are wild and unruly, given to looting, so that much of the livestock and provisions disappear, one knows not how.

'It was on a rainy afternoon. I was sitting in my room at the fort writing a long letter to an old friend in

Lucerne. Suddenly Mr Marshall burst into the room. He was drenched to the skin. I was very surprised to see him back already, for I had just sent a wagon loaded with foodstuffs and scrap iron up to Coloma. He said he had something very important to tell me and that he wanted to communicate it to me in the utmost secrecy; he begged me to conduct him to some isolated place, far from any possibility of being overheard or surprised by some indiscreet person. We climbed to the top storey, as he kept insisting that we must shut ourselves away in a remote chamber, even though there was nobody else at the ranch except my bookkeeper, who was downstairs in his office. Marshall asked me for something, I believe it was a glass of water, and I went down to fetch it for him. When I came up again, I forgot to lock the door behind me. Marshall had just that moment taken a rag out of his pocket, and was in the process of showing me a lump of some yellowish metal that he had wrapped up in it, when my bookkeeper came into the room to ask me for some information. Marshall quickly hid the metal in his pocket. The bookkeeper apologized for disturbing us and left the room. "For God's sake, didn't I tell you to lock the door?" cried Marshall. He was beside himself and I had a hard time calming him down and convincing him that the bookkeeper had merely come in on business and not with the object of surprising us. This time, we bolted the door and even pushed a cupboard against it. And Marshall again took out the metal. He had several little grains of it, each weighing about four ounces. He told me he had said to the workmen that it might be gold, but they had all laughed at him and taken him for an idiot. I tested the metal in *aqua regia*, then I read the entire article on GOLD in the *Encyclopaedia Americana*. Thereupon, I announced to Marshall that his metal was gold, virgin gold.

'The poor boy almost went crazy. He wanted to jump on his horse at once and rush back to Coloma. He begged me to accompany him, post-haste. I pointed out that it was already dusk and that it would be better to spend the night at the fort. I promised to go with him the following morning, but he would not listen to reason and set off hell-for-leather shouting: "Come tomorrow, come early!" The rain was falling in torrents and he hadn't even stopped for a bite to eat.

'Darkness came down abruptly. I went back into my room. I was certainly not indifferent to this discovery of gold in the stream, in the foundations of my sawmill, no, indeed, but, like all the ups and downs of fortune in my life, I took it with a certain amount of detachment; nevertheless, I could not sleep that night, I was picturing to myself all the dire consequences and fatal repercussions that this discovery might have for me, but never for one moment did I imagine it would bring my New Helvetia to ruin! Next morning, I gave detailed instructions to my various work-crews and left at 7 a.m., accompanied by several soldiers and a cowboy.

'We were half-way up the winding track that leads to Coloma when we came across a riderless horse. A little higher up, Marshall emerged from the undergrowth. He had been halted by the storm and hadn't been able to go any further during the night. He was perished with cold and half dead from hunger. However, his exaltation of the previous evening had not subsided.

'We went on up the track and arrived at this famous El Dorado. The weather had cleared up a little. That evening, we made a tour along the banks of the canal; the rain had swollen the waters and both sides were awash. I operated the sluices, the canal emptied instantly and we went down into the bed to search for gold. We found plenty of small particles and several workmen even handed me small nuggets. I told them I would have a ring made from this gold as soon as it became possible to have this done in California and, in fact, I did have this ring made, much later, in the form of a signet-ring; in default of a family crest, I had my father's printer's mark engraved on it, a phoenix being consumed in the fire, and inside the ring was the following inscription:

THE FIRST GOLD DISCOVERED IN JANUARY 1848

Then three bishops' croziers, the Basle cross, and my name: SUTTER.

'The following day, I rode round the whole extent of Coloma, taking careful note of its situation and the lie of the land, with particular reference to the water-courses, then I called all my people together. I explained to them that it was necessary to keep this discovery a secret for a further five or six weeks, to give me time to complete the construction of my sawmill, on which I had already spent 24,000 dollars. When they had given me their word of honour, I returned to the ranch-house. I was unhappy and had no idea how to extricate myself from this ill-fated discovery of gold. I was certain that such a business could not be kept secret.

'And I was right. Barely two weeks later, I sent a white man up to Coloma with a load of tools and provisions; some young Indian boys escorted him. Mrs Wimmer told him the whole story and her children gave him some grains of gold. On returning to the fort, this man immediately went to the stores, which were situated outside my enclosure, and asked Smith for a bottle of brandy. He wanted to pay for it with the grains of gold he had brought down from Coloma. Smith asked him if he took him for a dingo dog. The carter told Smith to come and ask me, if he didn't believe him. What could I do? I told Smith the whole story. His partner, Mr Brannan, sought me out at once and asked me a whole heap of questions, which I answered truthfully. He ran out without even bothering to shut the door. During the night, he and Smith loaded all their merchandise into wagons, stole some of my horses and left in haste for Coloma.

'After that, my workmen began running away.

'Soon, I was left alone at the fort with a few faithful engineers and eight sick men.

'My Mormon employees were more reluctant to leave me, but when gold fever infected them too, they threw their scruples to the wind.

'Now, beneath my windows, there was an unending procession. Every man who could walk came up from San Francisco and the other shanty-towns on the coast. Everyone closed up his hut, his cabin, his farm or his business and made his way to Fort Sutter, then up to Coloma. In Monterey and the other towns in the South, they believed at first that the whole thing was an invention on my part to attract new settlers. The procession on the road stopped for a few days, then it began again, worse than before, as these towns also joined the march. Whole townships were emptied; my poor estates were swamped.

'So began my miseries.

'My mills were at a standstill. The very millstones had been stolen from me. My tanneries were deserted. Large numbers of leather hides, in the process of preparation, were going mouldy in the cellars. Raw hides rotted away. My Indians and my Kanakas ran away with their families. They all went prospecting for gold, which they exchanged for brandy. My shepherds abandoned their flocks, my planters the plantations, the workers their many trades. My corn was rotting on the stalk; there was no one to pick the fruit in my orchards; in the byres, my finest milch-cows were mooing themselves to death. Even my loyal body of soldiers had fled. What could I do? The men came to see me, they implored me to leave with them, to go up to Coloma and search for gold. God, but it was a cruel blow to me! I left with them. There was nothing else I could do.

'I loaded my goods and provisions on to wagons and, accompanied by a clerk, some hundred-odd Indians and fifty Kanakas, I went up to establish my gold-prospecting camp in the mountains, on the banks of the creek that today bears my name.

'To start with, all went very well. But soon, hordes of rough-neck profiteers swooped down on us. They set up distilleries and ingratiated themselves with my men. I struck camp and moved ever higher up the mountain, but no matter what I did, that fiendish brood of distillers followed us everywhere and I could not prevent my poor Indians and my poor, wild natives from the Islands from tasting this new delight. Soon, my men were incapable of carrying out the simplest task; they drank and gambled away their wages, or the gold they had found, and spent three-quarters of their lives dead drunk.

'From the summit of those mountains, I could see the immense expanse of land I had brought under cultivation, now given up to looting and fire-raising. Even up there, in my solitude, I could hear the sound of pistol shots and, coming from the West, the hubbub of crowds on the march. At the far end of the bay, I could see them building an unknown town which grew larger before my eyes and, out in the roadsteads, the sea was full of vessels.

'I could stand it no longer.

'I went back down to the fort, having paid off all those who had run away and who did not wish to return with me. I cancelled all the contracts, and paid all the bills.

'I was ruined.

'I appointed an administrator of my estate, and, without even glancing at that rabble of parasites who had now installed themselves in my home, I left for the banks of the Feather River to see if my grapes were ripe. Only those Indians whom I had brought up myself accompanied me.

'If I had been able to follow my plans through to their conclusion, I should very soon have become the richest man in the world; as it was, the discovery of gold had ruined me.'

NINTH CHAPTER

32

On the 17th of June, 1848, General Mason, the new American Governor, leaves Monterey to go and see for himself how much truth there is in the fantastic rumours that are circulating about the gold-mines discovered in the Sacramento basin. On the 20th, he is in San Francisco. The town, recently so crowded, is now completely empty and deserted; the entire male population has gone up to the diggings.

'On the 3rd of July,' says his report, 'we arrive at Fort Sutter. The mills are standing silent. Immense herds of beef cattle and horses have trampled down their enclosures and are grazing peacefully in fields of wheat and maize. The farmhouses are falling into ruins, a nauseating odour wafts from them. The fort itself is very busy. Ferries and barges embark and disembark mountains of merchandise of every kind. There are camps of covered wagons all around the outer perimeter. Whole convoys arrive and depart again. People are paying a hundred dollars a month rent for a tiny room, and five hundred dollars a month for a wretched, single-storey hovel. The blacksmith and the shoeing-smith, who are still in Sutter's service, earn up to fifty dollars a day. Over an area of more than five miles, the slopes of the hills are covered with a multitude of tents that dazzle the eye in the glaring sunlight. The whole district is swarming with people. Everyone is panning gold, some with the aid of little saucepans or tightly-woven Indian baskets, others with the aid of the famous "cradles".'

The Polynesian, a newspaper issued in Honolulu, publishes a letter from which we quote the following extract:

'From San Francisco, our road led us through the valley of the Puebla as far as San José, a distance of some fifty miles. Never had I seen a more seductive country. The ground was dotted with flowers, a myriad of watercourses criss-crossed the prairies, the hills were covered with flocks of sheep. I had never seen such beautiful scenery. Then we passed the dilapidated buildings of the Santa Clara Mission, whose tiled roofs had caved in. We reached the banks of the San Joaquin, which we crossed by a ford; then we went up towards Fort Sutter, through country of astonishing fertility, which could support a huge population. But we did not encounter a single human being. All the farms were abandoned: the Americans, the Californians, the Indians, everybody was at the mining sector. After leaving Fort Sutter, we followed the steep banks of the American River and soon climbed the first foothills which rise up in terraces to the Sierra Nevada. At midday, we halted for lunch and a cup of coffee. While we were waiting for the water to boil, one of our company dipped his tin mug into a small creek that was running at our feet; it came up full to the brim with sand; he washed it and found four grains of gold at the bottom. By sunset, we had reached Captain Sutter's sawmill, where the first gold was discovered. We had just travelled twenty-five miles, through gold, silver, platinum and iron mines. The road was suitable for vehicles, even a town carriage could have negotiated it easily, and it ran through fairy-tale landscape, decked in flowers and traversed by thousands of little streams. I found a thousand white men there, busy panning gold. The average yield is about one ounce per man per day, and each prospector makes about sixteen dollars. The deeper one digs, the higher the yield. At the moment, the record for the luckiest strike is held by a man who made himself two hundred dollars in a single day. The nuggets come in all sizes: the largest that has been extracted weighed sixteen ounces. All the mountains in this area contain gold and platinum. At a distance of five miles from this sawmill, they have just discovered the richest seam of silver ever known. These treasures are inexhaustible. . . .'

33

At news of these prodigious lodes, the Yankee spirit of enterprise came to the boil. In New York and Boston, ten thousand emigrants gathered, bound for California. In New York City alone, sixty-five societies were founded to exploit this new business. Sons of the wealthiest families invested in it and the capital amassed was counted in millions. In the space of a fortnight, one small hotel on Broadway saw five hundred men file through its rooms, and every one of them was on his way to the Far West. By October, twenty-one vessels had already left the great port of the East destined for the Pacific coast; forty-eight others were preparing to set sail; on the 11th December, the hundredth sailed out of the Hudson. 'The whole of New England is on the move and making its way towards the ports or preparing to travel overland across the continent; we have given up trying to count the ships and the caravans,' cries the *New York Herald* of that date.

And what a journey!

34

Those who chose the land route had months of hardship and privation to look forward to. Others had to round Cape Horn – leaving New York Harbour, they headed due south, through the Gulf of Mexico, crossed the Line and sailed down the coast of South America as far as Cape Horn, the cape of storms, then had to turn and sail as far to the north again, following the coast of Chile, recross the Line and make straight for San Francisco – a voyage of 17,000 nautical miles which took between 130 and 150 days to accomplish.

But the majority of the gold-seekers crossed the Isthmus of Panama. A veritable human torrent sailed down the Gulf Stream and tramped the beaches of Cuba and Haiti before hurling itself upon Chagres, a hot and pestilent hole wallowing in the swamps. If all went well, it was possible to struggle on, through villages full of degenerate Indians or leprous Negroes, and reach Panama in three days, in spite of shifting sands, mosquitoes and yellow fever. Then, in furious haste, the survivors embarked for 'Frisco.

This traffic was so heavy that one New York company began to build a railway. Tons of earth and gravel had to be poured into the swamps and thousands of workers left their bones there, but the line was completed. It is true that the sleepers sank beneath the weight of the convoys but the trains got through nevertheless and the journey to San Francisco was shortened by several weeks.

At the head of the line, a town sprang up; it was named Aspinwall after the director of the enterprise. Regular communications, by steamship, were established with England, France, Italy, Germany, Spain and Holland. The little trains puffed their way to Panama, bearing cargoes of feverish Europeans who had come, dressed in red shirts, brown leather boots and corduroy trousers, to take their turn at tempting Dame Fortune.

San Francisco. California. Sutter!

Those three names echoed round the world, they were heard everywhere, even in the most secluded villages. They awoke men's appetites, their energies, their thirst for gold, their dreams and illusions, their spirit of adventure. And now, from every corner of the globe, solitary men were setting out, as well as sects, groups and corporations, all heading for the promised land, all converging on this EL DORADO where all one had to do was bend down and pick up gold, pearls and diamonds by the handful. On the quays of San Francisco South Americans, Kamchatkans, Siberian peasants and men from all the races of Asia, who had embarked in the ports of China, were arriving in a never-ending stream. Troops of Negroes, Russians, yellow men took their turn at occupying Fort Sutter, relieving the Germans, Swedes, Italians and French who had already gone up to the mines. People cohered into groups and multiplied with a rapidity unparalleled in history. In less than seven years, the inhabitants of the towns could be counted in hundreds of thousands and those of the whole region in millions. In ten years, San Francisco had become one of the largest capitals in the world. The little village of Yerba Buena had been swallowed up. Building land was fetching the same price as in London or New York.

Meanwhile, John Augustus Sutter was ruined.

35

Sutter's name is on the lips of everyone who travels up the Sacramento. Nevertheless, each man settles himself in the most propitious spot and there, where the soil offers up its treasures, plunges his hands in deep, grabbing all he can. Sutter's plantation, his farms, his entire domain, form a centre for the gold-panners. There are so many features inviting one to settle down there – the multitude of generous little water-courses, the judiciously-chosen site of the first farm, the extraordinary fertility of the soil, the tracks already laid out, the bridges and canals. One after another, villages spring into being. The fort crumbles into ruins. The very name of New Helvetia disappears. New names are given to the region and although Sutterville, Sutter's Creek and Sutter's County bear his name, Sutter himself does not see this as an act of homage but rather as a symbol of the ruination of his settlement and the calamity of his life.

36

John Augustus Sutter has retired into his Hermitage.

He has rescued what he could of his herds and flocks. In spite of events, the first harvest brings him in 40,000 bushels. His vineyards and his orchards seem to be blessed. He could still exploit all this, for there is a shortage of foodstuffs in the area, due to the massive immigration, and more than once the locust-cloud of gold-seekers is threatened with famine.

But Sutter's heart is no longer in the work.

He lets everything go.

His most faithful employees, his closest confidantes have deserted him. No matter how well he pays them, they can earn more in the mines. There are no longer any hands to tend the fields. There is not a single shepherd left.

He could, once again, make a fortune – speculate, profiteer in the astronomic rise in the price of edible commodities – but, to what purpose? He sees his stocks of grain dwindling and, presently, the end of his provisions.

Other men will make fortunes.

He lets things go.

He does nothing.

Nothing.

Impassively, he watches the seizure and partition of his lands. A new land registry is established. New title-deeds are drawn up. The latest arrivals are accompanied by men of law.

37

Since the cession of Texas and California to the United States, the government in Washington has extended the federal laws to these two territories, but there is a dearth of magistrates and, at the time of the gold rush, no authority has any hold over these cosmopolitan multitudes lusting for gold. When the Governor of Monterey sends in troops to maintain order, the soldiers lay down their arms, drop bag and baggage and desert to the mines, and if a warship, sent by the federal government to enforce respect for the law, disembarks an armed crew, they will vanish forever, drawn irresistibly to the mines. The commander cannot hold his sailors, not even with a wage of fifteen dollars a day.

The country is infested with thieves and bandits. The outlaws and the desperadoes lay down the only law – *their* law. It is the epic reign of the '45' and of summary justice. In the struggle for survival, might is right. Men are hanged with lassoes or shot down with revolvers. Vigilance committees are formed to protect the slowly-reviving civic life. Those who first took possession of the land can, as a last resort, go to Monterey to seek redress and have their property claims evaluated. The Governor addresses their just claims to the proper quarter and the government appoints a Commission of Inquiry. But Washington is too far away, the official commissions travel slowly, while the immigrants pour in in ever-increasing numbers, swamp the country, settle and multiply. By the time the gentlemen commissioners at last arrive on the spot, they can do nothing but report the overwhelming upheaval of men and affairs, total chaos where property is concerned, and if, by an unlucky chance, they take the time to study an individual case in detail, they are sure to be overtaken by events.

Ten large cities have sprung up. Fifteen hundred villages.

Nothing can be done.

Appeal to the Law.

The Law.

In September 1850, California officially enters the confederation of the United States. It is a State at last, a fully-fledged constitutional body, endowed with officials and magistrates.

And so begins a series of prodigious, costly and futile legal actions.

The Law.

The impotent Law.

The men of law whom John Augustus Sutter despises.

TENTH CHAPTER

38

Basle, late December, 1849.

In Basle, they still know nothing about the discovery of gold.

Frau Sutter is staying at the famous 'Stork Hotel'. Her three tall sons and her young daughter are with her. A devoted friend, tutor to her children during the long absence and even longer silence of their father, accompanies her. Frau Anna Sutter, *née* Dübeld, is a tall, dark-haired woman who hides her excessive sweetness beneath an air of severity. Round her neck, in a gold locket, she carries a daguerrotype of John Augustus, taken at the time when the couple were engaged.

Anna Sutter has taken a long time to make up her mind. A letter addressed from New Helvetia and dated end of December 1847, summons her to California. Detailed instructions for the embarkation and voyage are attached, as well as an important letter-of-credit on the Passavant, Sarrazin and Co. Bank in Basle. The fact that Anna Sutter is undertaking this voyage today is thanks to her father, the old pastor of Grenzach, who has urged her to it in the name of Christian charity and for the honour of her children; it is also thanks to the devoted care of Martin Birmann, the tutor, who has handled all the travel arrangements and legal formalities, who has made the journey to the bank in Basle several times to obtain the necessary information, and has just brought back from there not only a large sum of money, but sensational news. Today, Frau Sutter feels reassured, she knows that her husband, John Augustus Sutter, is a man of honourable reputation, accredited in the most important banks in Europe and that he is one of the largest colonists in America, the owner of an estate vaster than the entire canton of Basle, the founder of a country, the developer of a region, something like William Tell, for she cannot quite realize what New Helvetia is, and she has heard talk of war and battles; but what do her fears and her secret tremblings matter? She has been able to pay off all her husband's old debts and wipe out the infamous judgement of earlier times. Now, her duty calls her to a foreign land. She will obey that call.

The Chief Clerk of the Passavant, Sarrazin and Co. Bank has come to the hotel to bring her letters-of-credit on the banking houses of Dardel the Elder in Paris, and Pury, Pury and Son in Le Havre. He wishes Frau Sutter a pleasant journey on behalf of his directors and takes advantage of the occasion to speak to her about a cousin of his whom he would dearly like to see settled in America. The coachman is cracking his whip outside the front door. The proprietors of the 'Stork', Herr and Frau Freitag, are giving a farewell party in her honour and there is quite a gathering of worthy citizens, who are touched at the sight of this poor woman·setting off on such a long journey. They overwhelm her with recommendations and good advice. Lost in a huge, high-backed armchair, Martin Birmann is weeping and sneezing into his handkerchief. On his knees, he holds a tapestry travelling-bag fastened with a heavy padlock. At last, the whole family is installed in the post-chaise and Martin Birmann bestows the precious bag on Frau Sutter, giving her a complete list, once again, of all it contains.

The coach jerks forward. There are cries of 'Hurrah!'
The children laugh. The mother feels a great wrench at
her heart. Martin Birmann takes a double pinch of snuff
to hide his emotion.

Bon voyage!
Bon voyage!

39

The journey is swiftly accomplished. The post-chaise
travels hell-for-leather. The family spends the night at
Délémont. Next day, at Saint-Ursanne, they eat trout
for lunch, and while the children go into ecstasies over
the little town, which has preserved its medieval
ramparts, Frau Sutter feels her heart contract at the
thought that she is about to enter a Catholic country.
That night they sleep in Porrentruy. Then, next day,
into the land of the heathen, through the valleys of the
Joye and the Allaine to Boncourt, Delle and Belfort,
where they board the coach that comes from Mulhouse.

Now they gallop at full speed along the great highway
of France, and via Lure, Vesoul, Vitrey and Langres,
they reach Chaumont in time to catch the mail-coach to
Paris. From Chaumont, they could certainly have taken
the steam train which runs to Troyes, and from there
reached Paris by the Iron Way, but, in one of the
coaching inns, Frau Sutter has seen a leaflet containing
drawings by a certain Daumier, drawings which delineate
all the dangers to which this new mode of locomotion
exposes its passengers. That is why, despite her instructions, she boards the public coach that arrives from
Strasbourg; it is less dangerous, and besides, in this way

she will be able to remain a little longer amongst German-speaking people. The children, especially the boys, are disappointed.

In Paris, Dardel the Elder, her banker, warns her against too great a haste. It is in his home that she first hears of the discovery of gold. She is tempted to cry and run home to her father's house. Monsieur Dardel does not know exactly what is afoot, but he has heard that all the down-and-outs from Europe are going to California, and that they are fighting and murdering one another in the mines. He advises her to go no further than Le Havre and to obtain reliable information from his colleagues there before venturing to embark.

On the barge that sails down the Seine, there is a gang of men who look like cut-throats and gallows-birds; they form a little group apart from the other travellers. They are sitting on their luggage, talking quietly amongst themselves. Sometimes, furious arguments break out and one can hear, amidst shouts and imprecations, the words 'America, California, gold.'

Messieurs Pury, Pury and Son open their eyes very wide when they see Frau Sutter entering their office and learn from her own lips that she wishes to travel to New Helvetia.

'Why, yes, Madame, we know M. John Augustus Sutter extremely well, we are his commission agents and for many years have carried out substantial business deals on his behalf. Indeed, less than six months ago, we sent him a grand piano by sea. But things are changing, changing . . . we are not yet sure precisely what is happening; he is said to be the richest man in the world at the moment. It seems he has discovered gold, mountains of gold. We don't know exactly how much. Nevertheless, we feel it is our absolute duty to dissuade you from embarking just now to join him. This is hardly the moment to go to California. During the last three months, Le Havre has been invaded by all kinds of adventurers bound for that country, men without law or religion, men who have committed the most heinous crimes in the town. This is not the moment to expose your sons, still less your young daughter, to such dangers. No, no one goes via New York any more, it takes far too long. We ourselves have chartered three steamers that go direct to Chagres, it's a much shorter route. Everyone is using this route now, there have been 712 departures already this month. But do reflect, Madame, just think of the risks you will run in such company! Be patient for a few months, we will seek instructions concerning you from M. John Augustus Sutter personally. You could . . .'

But, in the face of Frau Sutter's mulish obstinacy, Messieurs Pury, Pury and Son cease to insist. They do whatever is necessary for her. Anna Sutter and her children embark on one of their steamers, *La Ville de Brest*, a paddle-boat which used to ply the Jersey run but has now been chartered by the new maritime line in Chagres for the transportation of would-be gold prospectors.

The crossing takes forty-one days. There are eleven members of the crew and 129 passengers, many of whom help with the handling of the ship. Frau Sutter and her daughter are the only women aboard. The passengers come from every country, but are predominantly Frenchmen, Belgians, Italians and Spaniards. Five Swiss, nine Germans and one Luxembourger explain their enterprise to Frau Sutter in some detail. No, they have never heard of Sutter, but they have heard that California is a land full of gold, pearls and diamonds. You just have to bend down and pick them up. So-and-so and what's-his-name have already made their way there, they are simply following in their footsteps, and others, many, many more of them, will be coming on behind them. Some of the early birds are already rich, it seems, worth millions. 'There is gold everywhere, Madame, they are simply shovelling it up . . .'

Aspinwall. Heat, humidity, humidity, heat. There are seventeen steamers in the roads, flying the flags of nine different nations. New York, Boston, Philadelphia, Baltimore, Portland, Charleston, New Orleans: the American hordes storm the little train from Panama. They shout, they yell, they jostle one another and while the engine is panting its way through the swamps, under a dense cloud of steam, passing the mud huts full of squint-eyed Indians and Negroes with suppurating limbs, a rude chant arises, keeping time with the rhythms of the train and bawled by a thousand male voices:

To 'Frisco!
To 'Frisco!
Sutter. Sutter. Sutter. Sutter.
Sutter. Sutter. Sutter. Sutter.
To 'Frisco!
Sszzzzz. K. Sszzzzz. K. Pug!
Welcome back again!

Anna Sutter clasps her daughter tightly in her arms. The boys lean out of the window to see the poisonous snakes in the swamps. A Dane and a German, coming down from New Brunswick, recount what they know of the great Captain Sutter. He is a king; he is an emperor.

He rides on a white horse. The saddle is made of gold, the bit is gold, the stirrups, the spurs and even the horseshoes are also of gold. In his house, it is a perpetual feast-day and they drink brandy all day long. Frau Sutter faints away, her heart has ceased to beat. By the time she arrives in Panama, one lock of her hair has turned white.

The sun is like a molten peach.

Panama to 'Frisco aboard a sailing-ship. The crew are frightful-looking Kanakas, they fill her with dread. They are hideously maltreated. The skipper, an Englishman, cuts off the thumb of one of them to tamp down the tobacco in his pipe. As they draw near to the land of gold, the passengers become so excited that quarrels flare up over nothing and knives are quickly drawn. Frau Sutter is seized by an ague, a trembling in her limbs that lasts all the way to 'Frisco.

In San Francisco, she learns that New Helvetia no longer exists and that Sutter has disappeared.

40

Women. There are women who work the gold-diggings, jolly, rough wenches who are no better than they should be and who toil and die of over-work just like the men. They slave, blaspheme, swear, smoke pipes, spit and chew coarse black tobacco while wielding the pick and shovel all day long, so that they can go boozing at night and lose their gold-dust at cards. One shouldn't admire them too much for they are even more vindictive and violent than the men; they are particularly touchy on affairs of honour and quite ready to defend their virtue with bullets, like those two Frenchwomen, legendary figures in the history of California, of whom Monsieur Simonin speaks in his *Relation d'un voyage en Californie* published in the *Tour du Monde* of 1862:

'. . . having spoken at length about the men, let us now spare a few words for the women, although their numbers in California are still very small.

'I will mention one, amongst others, whom the miners have nicknamed Joan of Arc. She works at the diggings like a man and smokes a pipe.

'Another, who is working a very productive claim, answers to the name of Marie Trousers, and owes this sobriquet to the masculine garment which she prefers to wear. . . .'

41

A blazing sun.

A small group is climbing up to Fort Sutter, led by an old Mexican. Three young men and a young girl on horseback are escorting a litter slung between two mules.

This journey has exhausted Anna Sutter. She cannot stop shivering. She is shaking with cold.

Her eyes are glazed.

'Yes, Madame, the Master is at his Hermitage, a property he has on the Feather River. It's a beautiful place. He's in his vineyards. You must take the route across country. I'll send a reliable guide with you, to lead you along the mountain tracks, so that you can avoid all these vagabonds and rascals who are amongst us now. My wife will act as your guide, she's an Indian and knows the whole area. Please tell the Master that Wackelnager himself, the manager, has abandoned everything to go in search of gold, and that Ernest, the shoeing-smith who was working with me till recently, has left too. Tell him I'm keeping an eye on everything and that I'm salvaging whatever can be salvaged. There's still plenty of money to be made here, but, for God's sake, let him tell me what he wants done! I'm all alone. Tell the Master it wouldn't be a bad idea if he came here himself and had a look around.'

It is Jean Marchais speaking, a Frenchman and the blacksmith of the fort. He has remained faithfully at his post, still working for his good master.

42

It is a beautiful California evening.

All day long they have been travelling through the abandoned farmlands of the Hermitage. Since leaving Fort Sutter, they have not encountered a living soul. This splendid domain, invaded by weeds and forest vegetation, is more tragic than the scrub of the mountains.

Now they come upon the silent mansion.

The party halts.

The only answer to the guttural cries of Sawa, the Indian woman, is the lugubrious howling of a dog. Finally, two Indians come out of the house, signalling with their arms.

The procession advances as far as the courtyard and the litter is set down.

'Mamma, Mamma!'

'Look, Mamma, we've arrived! Papa will be here in a minute. Sawa says he's been told of our coming.'

Anna Sutter opens her eyes. She sees everything on a huge scale – the immense empty sky, an alien land, a riot of vegetation and this great house that is strange to her.

A man comes out of the house, an old man.

Anna Sutter tries to sit up. She cries out:

'Johann!'

Immediately afterwards, there is a rattle in her throat.

Confused notions fill the poor brain of this pathetic woman. Everything is spinning round. Brightness and shadow. A great roar, as of rushing water, fills her poor head. She hears cries, and her memory receives a jolt. She remembers so many things now, and, suddenly, she distinctly hears the gentle voice of Jean Marchais, the blacksmith, giving her messages for his master. Then, humbly, she repeats his words, and John Augustus Sutter, who is bending over the head of his wife's litter, hears her murmur:

'Master . . .'

ELEVENTH CHAPTER

43

Father Gabriel, the protector of the Indians, has just spent several days at the Hermitage. This morning, he is leaving before dawn, for his mission calls him back to his savages. He is a stern man and his utterances are famous amongst the tribes; he lives with the Sioux, the Osages, the Comanches, the Blackfeet and the Snakes, who listen to him as to an oracle. He travels everywhere on foot. John Augustus Sutter accompanies him along the track into the Sierra, as far as Round-Stone.

At the moment of parting, Father Gabriel grasps his hand and says to Sutter: 'Captain, a portion of the world's history has fallen on your shoulders, but you're still standing upright amidst the ruins of your former power. Lift up your head, look about you. There are thousands of people disembarking daily and coming here to work, hoping to find fortune and happiness. A whole new life is springing up in this country. You must set an example. Courage, old pioneer, this land is your true fatherland. Begin again!'

44

If Sutter has once more set his shoulder to the wheel, it is not for his own sake, but for his children's. He builds the farm of Burgdorf for his son Victor and that of Grenzach for his son Arthur. Mina, his daughter, will have the Hermitage. As for his eldest son, Emile, he has sent him East to study law.

Father Gabriel supplies the necessary labour force for this renewed burst of activity; with his revered eloquence, he has managed to tear crews of Indians and Kanakas away from the distilleries and the gold-mines. The Hermitage is now a Temperance Centre for the savages and the islanders.

The yellow races are also being taken on in ever-increasing numbers.

And prosperity is reborn. But it is not destined to last long.

45

John Augustus Sutter cannot forget the blow that has struck him down. He is a prey to morbid terror. More and more, he holds himself aloof from the work on the farm and this new enterprise no longer absorbs all his faculties, as it once did. The whole business scarcely interests him any more and his children are probably quite capable of succeeding on their own, as long as they heed his advice. He himself plunges into a study of the Book of Revelation. He asks himself a multitude of questions which he cannot answer. He believes that, all his life, he has been an instrument in the hands of the Almighty. He is seeking to discover the purpose, and the reason for this. And he is afraid.

He, the man of action *par excellence*, he who has never hesitated, hesitates now. He becomes withdrawn, distrustful, sly, avaricious. He is full of scruples. The discovery of the gold-mines has turned his hair and beard white; today, his tall figure, his bearing as a leader of men, are bowed and curved beneath the weight of a secret anxiety that gnaws at his soul. He dresses in a long woollen robe and wears a little rabbit-skin cap. His speech has become halting, his eyes shifty. At night, he does not sleep.

Gold.

Gold has ruined him.

He does not understand.

Gold, all the gold that has been extracted during the last four years and all the gold that will be extracted in future, belongs to him. They have robbed him. He tries to make a mental estimate of its value, to arrive at a figure. A hundred million dollars, a thousand million? Oh, God! His head spins at the thought that he will never see one cent of it. It is an injustice. Lord, Lord, to whom can I turn for help? And all these men who have come here to ruin my life . . . why? They have burned down my mills, pillaged and devastated my plantations, stolen and slaughtered my flocks and my herds, laid waste all the fruits of my Herculean labours . . . is this just? And now, after murdering one another, they are founding families, building villages and towns and settling themselves on my lands, under the protection of the Law. O Lord, if this is right, if this is in the order of things, why cannot I, too, profit from it, and what have I done to deserve such total ruin? All these towns and villages belong to me, after all, as well as the people and their families, their work, their livestock, their fortunes. My God, what can I do? Everything has crumbled to dust between my fingers – possessions, fortune, honour, New Helvetia and Anna, my poor wife. Is it possible, and why?

Sutter seeks help, advice, something to hold on to, but everything slips from his grasp. At times, he even reaches a point where he believes all his misfortunes to be imaginary. And then, by a strange inward turning upon himself, he dreams of his childhood, his religion, his mother, his father; he dreams of all that respectable, hard-working background, and above all of his grand-father, that upright man, dedicated to order and justice. And he feels ashamed.

He is the victim of a mirage.

More and more often, he returns in thought to his distant homeland; he dreams of that peaceful little corner of old Europe where all is calm, well-ordered and methodical. There, everything is in its appointed place, the bridges, the canals, the roads. The houses have been standing forever. The lives of the inhabitants are uneventful: they work, they are content with their lot. He sees Rünenberg again, as if in a painting. He thinks of the drinking-fountain he spat into on the day of his departure. He would like to go back there and die.

46

One day, he writes the following letter:

'My dear Herr Birmann,

'My children have written to you about the terrible misfortune that had already struck me when my poor Anna came here to die on my doorstep. It was the will of Divine Providence to have it so. But do you know the full extent of my miseries? I do not want to keep harping on the story of this catastrophe which is, in effect, the story of my whole life. God knows, I have puzzled over it enough in my mind during the last four years, and yet, I assure you, I cannot make head nor tail of it. I am not one to complain and yet it is a sorry sort of creature who writes to you, broken, worn out, exhausted, like an old work-horse. All the same, I must tell you that I have in no way deserved what has befallen me; whatever errors I committed in my youth, I have paid for with years of adversity. Let me explain that I lived in this country like a prince, or rather, in the words of our old proverb, I lived in this beautiful land of California "like God in France". It was the discovery of gold that ruined me. I do not understand it. The ways of Our Lord are devious and mysterious. It was my carpenter, Mr Marshall, who first brought the gold to light one day when he was working on the foundations of my sawmill at Coloma. After that fatal blow of his pickaxe, everyone deserted me – clerks, labourers, storemen, even my brave soldiers and my trusted personal assistants, in spite of the fact that I paid them all good wages. But they wanted more, and they robbed me, looted my property, then went off to search for gold. Gold is damned, and all those who come here, and all those who mine the gold are damned, for the majority of them disappear, and I ask myself how and why this happens. Life has been hell here during recent years. Men cut each other's throats, steal from one another, murder each other. Everybody has turned to banditry. Many have gone mad or committed suicide. And all this for gold, gold that is transformed into brandy, and after that into God knows what. Today, it seems as if the whole world is on my estates. Men have come from every country on earth, they have built towns, villages and farms on my lands and they have divided my plantations amongst them. They have built a city of the damned, San Francisco, at the very spot I had chosen for the disembarkation of my poor Kanakas, who have also run off to look for gold and barter it for liquor. Most of them would have died like dogs by now were it not for the good Father Gabriel, who went after them and saved them from the clutches of Shannon, the king of the distillers, and brought them back to me, often at the risk of his life. I gave them work, and now they are employed at the Hermitage, alongside my good Indians, and on the two farms I have given to my sons, Victor and Arthur, as they have no doubt written and told you.

'Today, California is part of the American Union and the country is in a state of complete transformation. Loyal troops have arrived from Washington, but they have much to do yet before order is restored. Every day, newcomers arrive and there are still mountains of gold. As I have already said, most of the earlier arrivals have disappeared, nobody knows how. The Beast of the Apocalypse is roaming through the countryside now and everyone is very agitated. The Mormons have already departed with their carts laden with gold, and I had no heart to follow them. It is said they have built a city on the shores of Salt Lake, where they live now in debauchery and drunkenness, for they have planted vines, which they learned to do in my vineyards, where many of them worked before the gold was found. In those days, they were good men and responsible workers, but now it seems they too are damned. Am I really to blame for all this? There are moments when, pondering on my misery, I believe that I am. Bands of strolling players are also wandering about the countryside, and many women come here, Italians, Chileans and Frenchwomen, some of them looking for husbands, but they do not all stay. The first men to stake claims to

91

the land are all in litigation with lawyers in New York, who are issuing title-deeds to the new arrivals. Everybody is bringing lawsuits. For myself, I do not know what to do, I don't want to be just like the rest, but what should I do? This is why I am writing to you.

'This is the position:

'I am ruined.

'According to American law, one half of the gold extracted is mine by clear right, and we are talking about hundreds and hundreds of millions of dollars' worth. Moreover, I have suffered an incalculable loss through the discovery of gold on my lands; my property has been overrun, devastated and despoiled, I am therefore entitled to compensation. In the third place, I am the sole proprietor of the terrain on which San Francisco has been built (apart from a narrow strip of land along the ocean-front which belongs to the Franciscan Mission) and of other sites on which towns and villages have been built. I possess all the title-deeds to these lands, which were given to me in the time of the Mexicans by Governors Alvarado and Micheltorena by way of reward for my services and in payment of my expenses at the time of the wars with the Indians on my northern frontier. Fourthly, hordes of new settlers have taken possession of my plantations and exhibit title-deeds which are flagrantly new, whereas I was the one to bring this entire region under cultivation, and I paid the Russians dearly for their small farms when they left. And lastly, the bridges, the canals, the ponds, the locks, the tracks, the roads, the harbour, the landing stages and the mills that I had constructed at my own expense, today serve the public welfare, so the State legislature must pay me for them. There remains also the question of all the gold that will be mined during the next quarter of a century, and over which I have some rights.

'What should I do?

'It makes me ill to think of the sum that all this must represent.

'The trouble is, if I begin, it will be not one but a thousand lawsuits I must bring all at once; I must attack tens of thousands of individuals, hundreds of communities, the legislature of the State of California and the government in Washington. If I begin, it will be not one, but ten, a hundred fortunes that I will have to spend, although it is true that what I am claiming would make it all worth while (even before the discovery of gold, I was on my way to becoming the richest man in the world). If I begin, it will not be one new country I shall have to conquer, as it was when I landed for the first time, all alone, on the sands of the Pacific, but the entire world. They would all be against me, and I should have to fight for years and years, and I am beginning to feel my age, I am already hard of hearing, I fear my strength might let me down, and it is for this reason that I have sent Emile, my eldest son, to the Faculty of Law, for it is on him that all this immense business of the gold will devolve and, being on the inside, so to speak, he will know better how to avoid the traps and pitfalls of the law, and those men of law whom his simpleton of a father greatly fears. Yes, I confess it.

'As a matter of honour, I cannot lose everything, let it all go, just like that, without a word. It would be a crying shame, an injustice!

'On the other hand, I often ask myself whether I have the right to intervene, or whether there are not too many human interests at stake which are beyond my understanding, and if God who reigns in Heaven has not some particular design for all these people whom He sends into this country? And I myself feel that I am lost in His hand.

'What should I do?

'Gold brings misfortune. If I touch it, if I pursue it, if I claim what is mine by indisputable right, shall I not be damned in my turn, like so many others whose example I have before my very eyes and of whom I have already spoken to you?

'Tell me, what should I do? I am ready for anything. To disappear. Abdicate. I could, on the other hand, set to work again and give useful support to Victor and Arthur, who are making very good progress. I could squeeze the maximum produce out of my farms, small-holdings and plantations, open up new areas of cultivation, extend the work of my Indians and Kanakas, throw myself into new speculations – in a word, make the necessary money for the lawsuits and press on till my strength is exhausted. But is all this really necessary? I am homesick. I dream of our beautiful little canton of Basle and would like to return there. God, how lucky you are, my dear Herr Martin, to be able to stay in your own home! I could sell the two farms and the Hermitage, liquidate everything, come home and settle the children in Switzerland. Should I do it, or would it be desertion, and have I the right to abandon this country to which I have given life and which, I feel, will rob me of my own? Tell me what I should do, dear Herr Martin Birmann, and I will follow your advice to the letter and obey you in everything, blindly.

'I am addressing myself to you because Father Gabriel mentioned you when he came to the farm to give my poor Anna decent Christian burial. He told me he knew you in his childhood. I believe he is a native of your village; from what I have heard, his name must be

März, but I am not too sure as he is as secretive as the Indians, to whom he is devoted body and soul, and he never speaks about his own people, except that once to tell me that he remembered you very well. In earlier days, when I was fighting on the frontier, he was my worst enemy; he bore me a grudge, resenting the fact that I, a compatriot, was making the Indians work, and bringing in Kanakas as forced labour, but, later on, he understood that I could never have achieved anything without them, and that they, for their part, could not have survived without me, once the Mexicans had abandoned them. As for the Kanakas, I have never been a wicked man, and Father Gabriel has been able to see that for himself. At the moment of my terrible misfortune, when all were deserting me, he was the only one to stand by me and he remained faithful to me from then on. Even now, it is only thanks to him that my children have been able to set up their establishments. He is a saint, may God keep him in His holy care, and may He keep you, too, dear Herr Martin Birmann, and bless you for having been a father to my children for so many years. Today, it is in the name of these same children that their father implores your advice: what should I do?
'Amen.
'Your brother in Jesus Christ,
'John Augustus Sutter, Captain.'

47

John Augustus Sutter does not wait for a reply from the worthy old Martin Birmann, a solicitor by calling and voluntary treasurer of the community of John the

Baptist in his little village of Botmingen, in Basleland. John Augustus Sutter begins a lawsuit.

His lawsuit.

A lawsuit that revolutionizes the whole of California and comes near to throwing the very existence of the new State into jeopardy. Everyone is passionately involved. Everyone has a personal interest in the case.

Above all else, John Augustus Sutter lays claim to exclusive ownership of the territories on which towns like San Francisco, Sacramento, Fairfield and Riovista have been built. He has had these lands valued by a committee of experts and claims 200 million dollars. He issues summonses against 17,221 individuals who have settled on his plantations, demanding that they vacate their premises and pay him damages with interest. He claims 25 million dollars from the legislature of the State of California for having taken over the roads, tracks, locks, mills, canals and bridges, and the installations in the Bay, and having placed them at the disposal of the public. Also, an indemnity of 50 million dollars from the government in Washington for its failure to maintain public order at the time of the discovery of the gold-mines; failure to stem the flood of the gold rush; failure to control their own Federal troops, who were sent into the area and deserted in gangs, thus becoming the principal element in the disorder and amongst the most ruthless looters; failure to take appropriate measures to reimburse both the State and Sutter personally for their share from the output of the mines. He submits, in the first instance, that he has rights to part of the gold extracted up to the present time and asks that a commission of jurists give an immediate ruling on the amount of gold due to him out of that which will be extracted from this day forth. He does not ask for any personal sanctions against anyone at all, neither those people in authority who have failed in their duty of seeing that the law is respected, nor police officers incapable of upholding public order, nor prevaricating officials. He bears no man a grudge, but he demands justice, simple justice, and, in bringing his case to Law, he is putting all his trust in jurisprudence.

Emile has come back from the University and is devoting himself exclusively to this monstrous affair. He is assisted by the four most eminent legal experts in the Union. In his offices at the corner of Commercial Street and the Plaza Mayor, in the heart of San Francisco, he is surrounded by a flock of solicitors, clerks and scribes.

The cities put up their defence. San Francisco, Sacramento, Fairfield, Riovista and even the smallest communities appoint barristers for life, solely to concern themselves with this particular case, and to oppose Sutter's claims with all their strength and at all costs. Individuals band together, constitute defence syndicates, place their interests in the hands of the most famous lawyers, whom they bring out from the East at outrageous expense. Jurists are at a premium. Every member of the legal profession, down to the last shyster, is dragged in. In all the vast territories of the United States, one can no longer find a single barrister lacking his brief, nor a single man of law kicking his heels in a bar. Solicitors, notaries, bailiffs, articled clerks, scribblers and pen-pushers rush to California, where they swoop down like locusts amongst the cosmopolitan hordes of gold-seekers, who are still pouring in, for the rush is by no means over. This is a new rush, an unforeseen source of gold, and all these people are hoping to live off Sutter's lawsuit.

97

48

During this time, John Augustus Sutter never once sets foot in the capital. He remains on his property and he has recovered all his old energy and vitality. He draws on all his faculties and uses every weapon in his arsenal.

For he must have money, money and still more money to pay for all this legal red tape.

His lawsuit.

This lawsuit which is unfolding in the heart of San Francisco, the damned city which Sutter has never yet laid eyes on.

49

Four years go by, during which time the case follows its course before the tribunals.

Sutter manages to find the money for his insane legal costs.

All his enterprises are prospering. His small farms at Burgdorf and Grenzach supply San Francisco with milk, butter, cheese, eggs, chicken and vegetables. At the Hermitage, he has set up a fruit-preserving industry. His sawmills cut the planks and timber which are used in the building of the countless new villages. He has a nail factory, another for pencils. He sets up a paper-mill. Once more, he begins sowing acres of cotton and dreams of starting a spinning-mill.

The inhabitants of the country, already deeply in-debted to him, watch in terror as he amasses this new fortune and rises to ever more menacing power. Sutter is unpopular. Sutter is hated, but Sutter does not care. They cannot manage without his products and he squeezes the people as hard as he dare. 'Let them cough up, the dirty swine,' he is in the habit of saying when he is setting up some new business venture and anticipating its profits in advance. 'Let them cough up, then it will be they themselves who pay the costs of my case.' Nevertheless, by a strange paradox, this man who has such an insatiable need for money does not pan gold or distil liquor. On the contrary, he is in close contact with the religious sects of Philadelphia and leads an ardent temperance campaign amongst the Indians, the White and the Yellow races (he is dead against brandy, but not wine, of which the enormous quantity consumed in the region comes exclusively from his vineyards). And if any gold-diggers should happen to stray on to his property nowadays, he has them beaten without mercy, for they are the damned. Although he rarely opens it any more, the Book of Revelation is always buried in his pocket for, in spite of his crazy energy, there remains in the depths of his soul a great fear and, before God, he is none too sure of his rights.

Towards the end of the fourth year, his adversaries strike a first, terrible blow against him. The offices of his son Emile are burned down and all the riff-raff of San Francisco dance round the flames as if it were a celebratory bonfire. The entire country is jubilant when it learns that the principal documents pertaining to the case have been destroyed, notably the original title-deeds to lands granted by Governors Alvarado and Micheltorena. At this news, the new settlers squatting on his lands are ecstatic and the inhabitants of the towns and villages parade the streets shouting: 'We've run the wolves to earth! We've caught the old wolf by the tail!'

On the face of things, John Augustus Sutter takes this blow without flinching but, although he redoubles his efforts and gives orders for his case to be prosecuted with even greater vigour, he feels, in his innermost being, that his strength is secretly waning, while his fears wax full.

He has received yet another blow from the Almighty.

O, God!

I no longer have the strength to cry out. I will make no protest. Yet I cannot find it in my heart to submit. Do with me what Thou wilt.

I shall fight on.

TWELFTH CHAPTER

50

On the 9th of September, 1854, the entire population of California is in a carvival mood.

They are celebrating the fourth anniversary of California's entry into the Union and the fifth anniversary of the founding of the city of San Francisco.

Already, throughout the previous fortnight, crowds have been coming in by every route and from every corner of the state. The capital is adorned with garlands and lit with illuminations; the Star-Spangled Banner flutters from windows, from rooftops and on all the surrounding hills. At night, fireworks shoot upward to burst in a luminous, crackling shower; salvoes of musketry and artillery reverberate incessantly. The theatres – the Jenny Lind Theatre, the first building to boast a stone façade, and the Adelphi, where a company of French actors are strutting the boards – are constantly packed out. At every street corner, demagogues harangue immense crowds, inspiring them with prophecies of the prodigious future that awaits this new country and this new city. This entire young nation unites in a single sense of its own strength and power, in a sentiment of burning patriotism for the Union.

The bars are besieged and the well-known saloons packed to the doors, and it is in these haunts, the Arcades, the Belle Union, the El Dorado, the Polka and the Diana, that popular enthusiasm wells up and spills over into demonstrations in honour of John Augustus

Sutter. Committees and delegations are formed; colonists, planters, labourers, gold-diggers, women, children, soldiers, sailors and profiteers betake themselves to the Hermitage *en masse*, and there, under his very windows, they acclaim Sutter, invite him, take him captive, drag him out by force and carry him in triumph to the city.

Along the way, the old pioneer is saluted on all sides as 'The Ancestor'. The whole population of San Francisco comes out to meet him. The cannon booms, the bells ring, choirs celebrate his apotheosis. Men wave their hats in the air, women wave their handkerchiefs while showers of floral tributes flutter down from the balconies. Clusters of human beings, like bunches of grapes, are hanging out into the void, applauding, cheering and shouting hurrahs.

At the Town Hall, Mayor Kewen, surrounded by the highest Federal and State officials, solemnly awards John Augustus Sutter the title of General.

Then there is a procession through the town.

It is the greatest fête that has ever been celebrated on the shores of the Pacific.

All eyes are fixed on the tall old man who is riding at the head of the troops.

John Augustus Sutter is mounted on a big white horse. He is holding his general's baton in his hand. Behind him come his three sons, then the First Californian Regiment, then the mounted artillery and the Light Cavalry.

51

General John Augustus Sutter parades through the streets of San Francisco at the head of the troops.

He is buttoned up in a black frock-coat which is too tight for him; its long skirts flap over his horse's crupper. He is wearing checked trousers and boots with wide gussets. A broad-brimmed felt hat is rammed down on his skull.

As he crosses the town, General John Augustus Sutter is prey to a strange emotion. All these ovations, the hurrahs, the wreaths of flowers that fall at his feet, the bells, the songs, the cannon, the fanfare, the multitude, the windows full of women, the houses, the office buildings, the first palatial edifices and the interminable streets, all seem to him unreal. It is less than six years since he was living here in the midst of savages, surrounded by his Indians and his Kanakas from the Islands.

He thinks he must be dreaming.

He closes his eyes.

He does not want to see any more, he does not want to hear any more.

He allows himself to be led.

The procession carries him along to the Metropolitan Theatre where a monstrous banquet, and some fifty speeches, await him.

52

An extract from the speech by Mr Kewen, the first Mayor of San Francisco:

'. . . This pioneer, full of high courage and spurred on by a strange presentiment, detaches himself from the happy memories of his youth, drags himself away from the charms of his own home, abandons his family circle, leaves his native land to come, by untrodden paths, and throw himself into a country full of danger and adventure. He crosses arid plains beneath a scorching sun, he traverses mountains, valleys, rocky chains. In spite of hunger, fever, thirst, in spite of bloodthirsty savages who lie in ambush for him, or stalk him on the open prairies, he travels onward, his eyes ever drawn to that point in the sky where the sun plunges every evening into the Western ocean. This point draws him on like a magnet, he keeps his eyes fixed on it, as the traveller in the Alps of his beautiful homeland keeps his eyes fixed on the summit of the mountain covered in eternal snows, thinking of nothing, as he crosses abysses and glaciers, but the grandiose panorama and the pure, refreshing air which is found at these altitudes.

'And, like Moses on the summit of Pisgah in biblical times, he stands on the snowy crest of the sierra, and his vision clears and his soul rejoices; at last, he sees before him the Promised Land. But he is more fortunate than the Lawgiver of the Israelites, for to him it is given to enter this blessed land, and he descends from the mountain armed with new courage and fresh vigour to brave the solitude and the privations and, in gratitude, he dedicates this new land he has just discovered to God. To God, to liberty and to his beloved country, Switzerland.

'In the history of vanished peoples, and of the centuries that are gone, the names of certain great men, whom one can never forget, stand out. Epaminondas, whose virtue and love of country shed a glorious light over the deliverance of Thebes. Hannibal, the courageous, who led his victorious armies over the Alps and trod the classic soil of Italy, will long outlive the history of Carthage. In naming Athens, one names her divine sons, and the name of Rome is consecrated by the glory of illustrious men. Thus, in future times, when the pen of the historian wishes to trace the origin and foundation of our dear Fatherland, which by then will be one of the most powerful countries in the world, when the historian wishes to describe the suffering and the hardships of the beginning, and recount the struggle for liberty in the West, then one name will shine forth above all others: it is that of the immortal SUTTER!'

53

Speech follows speech.

General Sutter is absent, lost in his reverie.

The thunder of applause sets the rafters ringing in the huge theatre.

Ten thousand voices clamour his name.

Sutter does not hear.

He is fiddling nervously with the ring he is wearing, turning it round, changing it from one finger to another and repeating and repeating, over and over again under his breath, the inscription he has had engraved upon it:

- THE FIRST GOLD -
DISCOVERED IN JANUARY 1848

THIRTEENTH CHAPTER

54

The beginning of 1855, like the end of the previous year, marks a new triumph for John Augustus Sutter.

On the 15th of March, Judge Thompson, the highest magistrate in California, announces his verdict in the Sutter case.

He acknowledges Sutter's claims as being just and well-founded, recognizes the grants made by the Mexican governors as legal and inviolable and declares that all those immense territories on which so many towns and villages have been built are the personal, intangible and indisputable property of John Augustus Sutter.

This verdict, together with the reasons adduced, amounts to a small volume of over two hundred pages.

55

Jean Marchais is the first to bring news of this verdict to the Hermitage. He finds Sutter engrossed in a booklet on the breeding of silk-worms.

Immediately, Sutter pounces on his frock-coat and brushes it with long, vigorous strokes. In effect, this judgement is directed against the United States; it is therefore necessary to obtain ratification from the highest Federal Court, swiftly and without delay. He has not a moment to lose. Out of a sort of childish vanity,

Sutter is eager to reach Washington before the official courier arrives with the verdict. He will present himself to the Court in person.

'What a fine man this Judge Thompson is,' he says, as he dons his handsome embroidered shirt. 'O God, I have never doubted Thee!' he murmurs as he pulls on his boots.

'I thank Thee, I thank Thee,' he pronounces aloud.

Then he buttons up his gauntlets and buckles on his heavy belt with the revolver in its holster. 'At last, they are giving me justice.'

Justice!

He puts on his broad-brimmed felt hat and looks at himself in the mirror.

He is happy and, perhaps for the first time in his life, smiles at his own reflection.

He bursts out laughing at the thought of the trick he is going to play on the official courier by arriving in Washington ahead of him, and delivering the great news himself! 'God, what a bolt from the blue it will be!' I'll cross the Sierra by the mountain tracks; that way, I can see Father Gabriel and tell him the news. Now, there's another good man. How pleased he will be, and Shannon will have to bite his tongue. Those villains had better watch their step, from now on *we* shall be the ones to lay down the law here. I'll get Bill, Joe and Nash to ride with me, that'll be enough. I can stay with the Mormons *en route*, and, if I travel through Nebraska, Missouri and Ohio, I'll be in Washington in a flash. My three Indians must come all the way to the Federal capital with me, and we must appear on horseback. Unless the Mormons can take me down the Platte River to catch the train. I hear the railway's reached Des Moines already.

'Ah, they're good souls, good souls . . ."

In his haste, he does not even bother to advise his sons of his departure, and it is only as he is jumping into the saddle that he shouts to Mina, who has come running from the poultry-yard: 'Tell the boys I'm going to Washington. We've won, we've won! The case is over. Tell them, and send Marchais to them. We've done it at last! Goodbye, my darling, see you soon!'

And, with his three Indians in his wake, he sets off like a whirlwind along the track that leads to the Sierra.

John Augustus Sutter leaves everything behind him. He has his verdict.

56

The little party has been galloping all day long, and all night and all the following day They have barely given the horses time to breathe. On the second night, at about three in the morning, Sutter and his three Indians emerge from the great forests and reach the Mission Post which the good Father has built at the entrance to the col. The night is pitch black. There is not a star in the sky. Heavy clouds are hanging over the peaks of the Sierra. Men and horses are exhausted.

Father Gabriel is standing on the edge of the stone terrace that supports his little chapel. He is surrounded by Indians, men, women, children. They are all gazing in the same direction. To the north-west, the sky is ablaze. A great glow invades the lowering sky.

'God be praised, is it you, Captain?' cries Father Gabriel.

'General, General!' protests Sutter, jumping off his

horse. 'They have promoted me to General! It's all over now, I've won my case. Judge Thompson declared in my favour. I've won. It's in the bag. I'm going to Washington at once to have the verdict registered. The country is ours now, we shall be able to work. Everything can go ahead smoothly.'

'God be praised!' says Father Gabriel again, 'I was anxious for you. Look at that great light over there.'

Sutter looks.

There, far over there, a great gleam lights up the sky and reddens it fitfully. It is not a forest fire, for it is way over there on the plain; it is not a prairie fire, for it is not summer-time and the dry season is still a long way off; nor is it crops that are burning, for the fields are still barren and untilled. And that direction – due north-west! There can be no doubt, it is the Hermitage!

'Ach, the bastards!'

Sutter leaps on to his horse, jerks its head round and rides for home as if the devil were on his tail.

57

The moment Judge Thompson's verdict is known to the public, the entire city comes out on to the streets. Groups form at every corner and the bars and saloons are invaded by a crowd of vociferous drinkers. Violent arguments break out. Orators improvise speeches. Distillers offer 'drinks on the house', and stave in casks of brandy in the market-places. The mood of the mob becomes threatening. Sutter has too many enemies. Spokesmen of the party that opposed him and all the men of law who are in league against him incite the people, urging them to violence and mischief. Meetings are being held in every quarter of the town. In the evening, riots break out in San Francisco. The rioters set fire to the Law Courts, demolish the offices of the Clerk of the Court, destroy the Archives and storm the prisons. The populace are out to lynch Judge Thompson. Next day, the whole country is in a state of revolution and immediately men organize themselves into bands.

The authorities are powerless.

These people, who not so long ago acclaimed General Sutter, came to seek him out, to carry him off in triumph and give him a grand reception, an act of homage unique in the history of the United States, once more make their way to the Hermitage – but, this time, to attack it. There are about ten thousand of them and, as they advance, others hasten to swell the mob. The men are armed and there are wagons loaded with barrels of gunpowder. The Star-Spangled Banner floats above the heads of this disorderly multitude and it is to cries of 'Long Live America!' and 'Long Live California!' that everything in their path is pillaged, sacked, razed to the ground.

The Hermitage is burned down, the factories, workshops, sawmills, repair shops and windmills are blown up, the orchards chopped down, the irrigation pipelines perforated, the flocks and herds mown down by riflefire and any Indians, Kanakas or Chinese unfortunate enough to fall into the hands of the marauders are lynched without mercy. Anything that bears Sutter's trademark is obliterated. The plantations are put to the torch, the vineyards ravaged. Finally, they attack the wine-cellars. And the destructive fury of the mob turns vicious – they kill, they break, they burn, they sack with such utter ruthlessness that even the poultry are slaughtered by volley-fire. Then they go up to Burgdorf and to Grenzach, where they again wreak havoc, destroying everything, reducing it to ashes. They saw through the lock-gates, smash up the surface of the roads and blow up the bridges.

Ruins and ashes.

When Sutter returns home, four days after his departure, nothing remains of his vast enterprises.

Thin plumes of smoke still rise from the smouldering debris. Clouds of urubus, vultures and crows with bloodied beaks squabble over the carrion of horses and cattle littered about the fields.

From the branch of a wild fig-tree swings the corpse of Jean Marchais.

This time, all is lost.

Forever.

58

Sutter contemplates the disaster with a mournful eye.

John Augustus Sutter is worn out. His life, his suffering, his hardships, his energy, his will, his endurance, his work, his perseverance, his hopes have all been in vain. His books, his papers, his instruments, his weapons, his tools, his bear and puma skins, his furs, his walrus tusks, his whalebones, his stuffed birds, his collection of butterflies, his Indian trophies, his specimens of ambergris and of genuine amber, of auriferous sand, of precious stones and of minerals of all kinds have been reduced to a heap of hot ashes.

Everything that he holds most dear, everything that represents the life and the pride of a man, has gone up in smoke.

General John Augustus Sutter no longer possesses anything of his own, except the clothes on his back, his viaticum and the Book of Revelation in his pocket.

He, who had hoped to become the richest man in the world!

Overcome with self-pity, he weeps for a long time. He is a broken man.

59

And suddenly he thinks of his children.

Where are they? What has become of them?

Then he begins to wander through the district, from farm to farm and village to village. Everywhere, they sneer at him, mock him, turn their backs on him. The people insult him. The children throw stones.

Sutter steels himself, says nothing, takes it all, the spite and the abuse.

He has a crushing sense of guilt.

He mumbles a prayer: 'Our Father, Which art in Heaven . . .'

He has fallen into a second childhood.

He is a pathetic old man.

60

Months pass. And then one day his sorrowful wanderings bring him to San Francisco.

He enters the city without being recognized by a soul.

He is frightened by the tall houses that rise up on either side, the intersecting streets, the swiftly-moving vehicles, the hurrying people who jostle him. Above all, he has a horror of the human face and is afraid to raise his eyes.

Misfortune dogs his footsteps.

He sleeps in the port and begs in the outer suburbs. He spends hours hanging about the waste ground where, only yesterday, stood the offices of his lawyer son.

One day, mechanically and without thinking, he goes in to see Judge Thompson. He finds his daughter, who has been given refuge there. Mina is in bed, she is suffering from nervous shock and has difficulty in expressing herself.

There, too, he hears news of his sons. Victor has again taken ship for Europe. Arthur was killed defending his farm. As for Emile, the eldest son, the lawyer, the one who had the whole business at his finger-tips and conducted the lawsuit, he has committed suicide in some squalid hovel.

As Sutter is stone deaf, he asks them to repeat this painful story twice.

'Thy will be done. Amen.'

FOURTEENTH CHAPTER

61

At the foot of the Twin Peaks, there stands a large white house whose pediment and Ionic columns are made of wood. It is surrounded by a spacious park and flower gardens. This is the country home of Judge Thompson; he loves to spend his weekends there, inspecting his young rose-bushes with a volume of Plutarch under his arm. It is in this retreat that Sutter, little by little, is restored to life and consciousness.

His legs are weak and he has put on an enormous amount of weight. White locks tumble over his stooping shoulders. His left side is afflicted with a slight tremor. His eyes water perpetually.

Mina has made a quick recovery from her terrible shock, the natural resilience of youth and the maternal care of Mrs Thompson have sufficed to restore her. She is engaged to Ulrich de Winckelried, a young dentist; the wedding is fixed for Christmas, and she is so happy about it that she cannot abide the sight, nor the presence, of her old, broken-down father. That is why she stays with the Thompsons in their town house, where these good people, so simple, so cheerful, so human, are always ready to guide and advise her in the setting-up of her new household.

Once again, John Augustus Sutter is all alone.

62

He paces to and fro beneath the trees or stands for hours in contemplation before a newly-blossomed rose. He never speaks to anyone. Sometimes, he will stop without ceremony in front of one of the gardeners, make a gesture as if to ask him something, then turn his back and walk away without opening his lips. The wind stirs the skirts of his frock-coat. He seeks the most secluded alley-ways to walk in. In the distance, the boom of the Pacific surf can be heard.

Twice a week, Judge Thompson comes out to see the General.

63

In all the vast territories of the United States, Judge Thompson alone understands and feels compassion for the plight of the General. Thompson is an enlightened man with a broad and well-balanced outlook; he fulfils his duties with the utmost integrity. Having made a thorough study of Greek in his youth, he has preserved a love for the humanities, a lofty system of reasoning and a taste for logical, unbiased deduction that he is capable of carrying to its ultimate conclusion. His mind is naturally inclined towards the contemplative mode. Thus he grasps the tragic aspect of John Augustus Sutter's life.

He has taken all the General's interests into his own hands, reviewed the whole affair and spent entire nights bent over the dossiers of the case. He has nothing with which to reproach himself. His verdict was arrived at in a full knowledge of the facts, according to the dictates of his conscience as a man and as a high court magistrate; in all equity, he pronounced in accordance with the letter and the spirit of the law. But, but . . . today, he understands that it is not so much a question of law as of saving a man, an old man, and he listens to the counsels of his heart. And when he comes to see the General, he makes a point of preaching reason to him.

Meanwhile, he offers him a refuge and sees to it that he gets all the care and attention his condition requires.

64

'Listen, General, you've suffered enough, don't persist with this business that has brought you nothing but misery. This is what I suggest you do, I've been thinking about it for a long time. Renounce all claims against individual persons. Give up all your proprietorial rights to those plots of land that passed long ago into other hands and are now registered in new names; give up once and for all any idea of getting your hands on your percentage of the gold extracted, or to be extracted in future – believe me, neither the State legislature nor the Federal government itself will ever succeed in collecting one red cent of it. Declare yourself ready to come to terms for, let us say . . . one million dollars' indemnity, payable in cash, and I will do everything in my power to obtain the money for you. If you're absolutely determined to work, you could very well demand new territory and you will get it easily; you know perfectly well the one thing we're not short of hereabouts is land, and, thank God, there's plenty of room still for newcomers. But don't go on with this futile business that will get you nowhere. You know as well as I do that there are too many vested interests, and everyone is intriguing against you in Washington. Trust me, and give up the game, it's not worth the candle.'

'Judge Thompson,' the General invariably replies, 'Judge Thompson, you judged the case and pronounced a verdict according to your conscience. And today you talk to me about money! Tell me, what am I suing for? I am suing for justice, nothing else. The highest court in this land must declare whether you were right or wrong. And it will pronounce. Besides, I am not appealing to mere man, but to God. I must carry this matter to the bitter end, for if I do not obtain justice in this world, it is a consolation to me to think that I will obtain it in heaven, and that one day I shall sit upon the right hand of the Lord.'

'But think of your children, think of Mina who is soon to be married. One day, she'll make you a grandfather.'

'Judge Thompson, a man like myself is damned and has no children. That is surely the sole error of my life. Arthur was killed, Emile committed suicide, and you told me yourself that we must consider Victor as lost, since he disappeared when the *Golden Gate* was shipwrecked in the open sea at the exit from the Magellan Straits. And, since I no longer possess anything, and cannot give her anything, I shall not be harming Mina by taking this matter to its conclusion; on the contrary, if I win, I shall have provided for my grandchildren and great-grandchildren and for seven times seven generations.'

'But what are you going to live on?'

'God, who has stripped me of everything, will provide for me as he nourishes the birds and the beasts.'

117

'I implore you not to leave here, you can stay as long as you like.'

'Yes, yes, I will go to Washington, at Christmas, after Mina's wedding. Then, we shall see whether there are any honest judges in Washington.'

65

Mina marries her dentist and the General departs for Washington, at Christmas, just as he has always said. He is armed with a recommendation from the Mayor of San Francisco, and, in his pocket, Judge Thompson's verdict keeps company with the little volume of the Book of Revelation. Thompson has also managed to persuade the State legislature to pay the old General a pension, a pension for life of three thousand dollars a year.

FIFTEENTH CHAPTER

66

The years pass. In Washington, the General has become a familiar figure; everyone knows that big, flabby body, those feet dragging along in down-at-heel boots, that old frock-coat, stained and sprinkled with dandruff, and that large bald head that wobbles beneath a battered felt hat. All Washington knows him, and every government bureau.

At first, thanks to the intrigues hatched by his enemies, he met with a rather frosty reception, but nowadays . . . well, so much water has flowed under the bridge, many of his adversaries have long been laid to rest and many of the officials transferred. Today, nobody is exactly sure what he wants – this mad old man, you know the one, the old General who fought in the war with Mexico and drivels on about gold-mines. He's certainly got a bee in his bonnet, a whole hive of them. And in the government offices it is a favourite sport to send him on from one department to another, knocking at endless doors. The General knows every nook and cranny of the law courts and all the staircases of the various Departments of the Administration; he comes and goes, climbs up, climbs down, knocking, rapping, waiting patiently outside closed doors; he walks thousands of miles, covers the same ground over and over again, retracing his steps, caught like a squirrel in a cage.

But he never abandons hope.

67

Throughout these long years, John Augustus Sutter has lived on his general's pension. 'Lived' is something of a euphemism, for, in reality, his pension has been gobbled up every year by shyster lawyers, shady business men and petty officials in the Administration who, one after the other, have promised to win his case for him.

In 1863, a young Danish swindler, just arrived from New York, meets Sutter at a religious assembly, takes his documents from him and, next day, introduces him to an accomplice who passes himself off as secretary to the Attorney-General. These two sharks get the old man completely into their clutches. Sutter writes to Judge Thompson, telling him his business is in the hands of God, and that the Attorney-General himself is to plead his cause. He asks for ten thousand dollars to pay the Attorney-General. Mina, to whom he has also written, sends him a thousand dollars. He manages to obtain probate and have his deceased wife's meagre dowry sent to him from Switzerland. All the money he collects is handed over to the two crooks, until one fine morning, seeing that there is nothing more to be got out of the old man, they disappear.

And still he receives frequent visits from lawyers, genuine as well as false, who get him to explain his affairs to them and then make him sign mountains of papers in which Sutter waives all claim to a quarter, a half, three-quarters or even the whole sum in case of success, for what does he care about money, gold, lands? It is justice he wants, a judgement, a verdict.

Years pass. Years of poverty and wretchedness. He works at all sorts of menial tasks in order to survive: he shines shoes, runs errands, delivers messages and washes dishes in a cheap eating-house for soldiers, where his title of general and his horror of whisky have made him popular. Nowadays, Mina sends him a hundred dollars a month and this money goes to every kind of tout and go-between, anyone who knows how to wheedle it out of him. He gives away every last dollar to set his lawsuit in motion.

In 1866, Sutter presents himself before Congress and claims one million dollars in cash and the restitution of his estates. He has been put up to this by a Polish Jew.

In 1868, Sutter sends an appeal to the Senate. He sets out the facts at great length and declares he will be satisfied with five hundred thousand dollars and his lands. This request is the brain-child of a sergeant of infantry.

In 1870, in a new appeal addressed to the Senate (which has been drawn up by a man named Bujard, a photographer from the Swiss canton of Vaud), Sutter claims no more than one hundred thousand dollars, renounces all other indemnities, gives up all rights to his lands and undertakes to leave the soil of the United States and return to Switzerland, where he will settle in the canton of Vaud, 'since I cannot,' he says, 'having once been the richest man in the world, return in poverty to my own canton and become a charge upon the parish of my forefathers'.

In 1873, he joins the sect of the Herrenhütter, entrusts his case to the Council of the Seven Johannite Elders and signs an act by which he donates all his eventual fortune and all his Californian possessions to the fraternity 'in order that the corrupting stain of gold may be washed away from these beautiful valleys by Adamite purity'. And the case starts up again, directed this time by a barrister who is both founder and spiritual director

121

of this German-American communist phalanstery.

Sutter leaves Washington and settles down in Lititz, Pennsylvania, in order to be baptised and purified according to the great Babylonian rite. He is now an immaculate soul and lives in intimacy with Our Lord.

68

The Herrenhütter of Lititz are established on large estates where an immense acreage of corn is grown and communally exploited. They also possess an oil-well. Sacks of corn and barrels of oil are sent down to the coast; by way of a trade-mark, they are stamped with the paschal Lamb *couchant*, holding a banner between its feet. On this banner, standing out in bold black type, are the initials J.C., which stand not for Jesus Christ, but for Johannes Christitsch, the founder, director and grand master of the sect. This man, a Serbian, contrives to function at the same time as a shyster lawyer and as a formidable, shrewd and enterprising business man; he is in the process of building up one of the largest industrial fortunes, on the backs of some four hundred 'enlightened ones', almost all of whom are of German origin.

The principal articles of faith in this phalanstery are: communal ownership of women and chattels, the regenerative sanctity of labour, certain rules of Adamite life and a belief in visions and states of possession. The only gospel is the Book of Revelation. That is why Sutter soon becomes famous in the little parish for his profound knowledge of this book, and for the personal interpretations he puts upon it.

69

The Great Whore that sitteth upon many waters is Christopher Columbus discovering America.

The Angels and Stars of St John are in the American flag and, with the inclusion of California, a new star, the Star of Absinthe, has come to be inscribed upon the Star-Spangled Banner.

The Anti-Christ is Gold.

The Beasts and the Satans are the cannibalistic Indians, the Caribbean natives and the Kanakas. They are also the Negroes and the Chinese, the black and the yellow races.

The Three Horsemen are the three great Redskin tribes.

Already, one-third of the immigrants from Europe have been decimated in this country.

I am one of the twenty-four Elders, and it is because I heard the Voice that I have come here amongst you. I was once the richest man in the world, I was ruined by gold . . .

A Russian woman lies at Sutter's feet in a state of ecstasy while he comments on the visions of St John and narrates episodes of his life.

70

But Sutter cannot even be left in peace to indulge this harmless folly.

Johannes Christitsch is his evil daemon, Johannes Christitsch, who has had the case reopened and is conducting the whole business, pushing ahead with it, determined to win no matter what the cost. Every week, Christitsch goes to Washington, where he intrigues, solicits, circulates officially-stamped documents, brandishes dossiers, rummages in the archives, brings new evidence to light and generally bestirs himself to set all this colossal procedure in motion once more. Very often, he brings Sutter with him, or sends him into town alone; he shows him off, puts him on exhibition and forces him to speak. He has appointed himself Sutter's manager. He has unearthed an old general's uniform and dressed Sutter up in it; he has even hung a few medals on his chest.

And the General's martyrdom begins again, as he goes from office to office, from one legal department to the next. Highly-placed officials take pity on the old man and his lamentable history, they take careful note of the case, promise to take steps on his behalf and see that he gets satisfaction. When he is on his own, all sorts of rogues stop him in the street and make him recount the tale of the discovery of gold, and Sutter becomes confused and mixes bits of the Apocalypse and Herrenhütter stories into the tale of his own life. He is completely unhinged; every urchin in Washington recognizes the General's madness and derives huge amusement from it.

The old madman.

The richest man in the world!

What a joke!

In 1876, thanks to Johannes Christitsch's relentless intriguing, Sutter is named Honorary President of the Swiss section at the Centennial Exhibition in Philadelphia. Christitsch takes advantage of this to establish relations with members of the Consulate; he dreams of instigating a diplomatic move to resolve Sutter's case.

In 1878, he and Sutter settle permanently in Washington. The affair is well under way, important political figures are concerning themselves with the case. Sutter has a kind of return to rationality, he is somewhat calmer and less prolix when he talks to people in the street.

At the end of January 1880, John Augustus Sutter is summoned to the Capitol and he learns that the Federal government is 'about to recognize your services forthwith'. In high places, they 'find your case interesting, your appeal just and your claims in no way exaggerated'. They are ready to award him a huge indemnity.

From this moment on, Sutter escapes completely from the clutches of Christitsch. He is once more very agitated and feverish. He cannot keep still for a moment, and wanders the streets night and day. He is constantly running to the Capitol. He besieges officials at all hours, asking if there is any news, if Congress has yet given its verdict. He is importunate, he badgers certain Congressmen, even in their own private homes, and is accompanied on these visits by a gang of ragamuffins who refuse to leave 'their' General's side, and who applaud whenever Sutter makes a scene, for nowadays he easily becomes violent and abusive and his little band delights in exciting him still further. The General is very proud of his popularity with the common people. In his mind, these children symbolize the Army of the Just.

'When I win my case, I shall give you all my gold,' he tells them, 'the gold that will be due to me, just gold, purified gold.'

God's gold.

72

One day, in the street, he runs across three male nurses who are taking a man to the asylum. He is a tall old creature, filthy dirty and dressed in rags, he is waving his arms about furiously, gesticulating and shouting. He manages to break free from his guardians and throws himself on the ground, rolling in the mud, filling his mouth, his eyes and ears with it and avidly plunging his hands into mounds of rubbish and ordure. His pockets are full of unspeakable filth and his bundle of possessions contains nothing but pebbles.

While the nurses are strapping him up, the General watches this man closely and suddenly recognizes him: it is Marshall, the carpenter. Marshall recognizes him too, and, as they are dragging him away, cries out to him: 'Boss, boss, I told you the truth – there is gold everywhere, everything is made of gold!'

73

On a hot afternoon in June, the General is sitting on the bottom step of the monumental stairway that leads up to the Capitol. His head is as empty as the heads of a great many old men; it is a rare moment of well-being, he is doing nothing but warm his old carcase in the sun.

'I am the General. Yes. I am the General . . . ral . . .'

All of a sudden, a child of about seven rushes down the great marble staircase, four steps at a time. It is Dick Price, the little match-seller, the General's favourite.

'General! General!' he shouts to Sutter, hurling himself on his neck. 'General! You've won! Congress has just delivered its verdict! They're giving you a hundred million dollars!'

'Is it true? Is it really true? Are you sure?' Sutter asks him, holding the child tightly in his arms.

'Of course, General, and it seems it's already in the papers. Jim and Bob have gone to get some to sell! Me, too, I'm going to sell lots of newspapers this evening, heaps of them!'

Sutter does not notice seven little guttersnipes who are splitting their sides with laughter beneath the tall portico of Congress and who are making signs at their little pal. Sutter rises to his feet, holds himself very erect, says but two words, 'Thank you!' then beats the air with his arms and falls down like a log.

General John Augustus Sutter died on the 17th of June, 1880, at three o'clock in the afternoon.

Congress was not even in session that day.

The urchins run away.

The hour strikes in the immense deserted square and before long, as the sun descends, the gigantic shadow of the Capitol falls over the General's corpse.

SIXTEENTH CHAPTER

John Augustus Sutter died at the age of seventy-three.

Congress never delivered a verdict.

His descendants never took any action, they abandoned the case.

His inheritance remains unclaimed.

Today, in 1925, and for just a few more years, there will still be time to come forward, take action, stake a claim.

Gold. Gold. Who wants gold?

Paris, 1910–1922.
Paris, 1910–1911.
Paris, 1914.
Paris, 1917.
Le Tremblay-sur-Mauldre,
from November 22nd, 1924
to December 31st, 1924.